KT-567-114

E S L

Newman History and Philosophy of Science Series

A PREFACE TO THE LOGIC OF SCIENCE

Newman History and Philosophy of Science Series

CHAIRMAN OF EDITORIAL COMMITTEE: M. A. HOSKIN

I I

A PREFACE TO THE
LOGIC OF SCIENCE

by

PETER ALEXANDER

SHEED AND WARD

LONDON AND NEW YORK

FIRST PUBLISHED 1963
UNDER THE AUSPICES
OF THE NEWMAN ASSOCIATION OF GREAT BRITAIN
(PHILOSOPHY OF SCIENCE GROUP)
BY
SHEED AND WARD LTD
33 MAIDEN LANE
LONDON W.C.2

This book is set in 11 pt. Ehrhardt

Made and printed in Great Britain by
William Clowes and Sons, Limited, London and Beccles

CONTENTS

FOR

CARYL AND MEYRICK

PREFACE

I have been mainly concerned with purely logical
conceptions but in the course of the book I have given
notice of some of the major problems in the philosophy of science. I have made no attempt to solve any
of these problems and few attempts even to clarify

PREFACE

This is not a textbook of the philosophy of science;
it is a brief and elementary treatment of certain
conceptions, most of them purely logical, which are
essential in the philosophy of science. Many British
universities now provide courses in the philosophy
and history of science which are designed especially
for students of the sciences, who often have no other
official contact with philosophy. These students are
unlikely to have the necessary knowledge of logical
conceptions which a lecturer in the philosophy of
science would like to be able to assume, especially if
his course is a short one. The book has been kept small
for pedagogic reasons and not merely in order that it
shall fit into this series. In my own bitter experience,
many students will not, or do not have time to, read
one of the standard textbooks of logic if their course
in the philosophy of science is, as is often unfortunately the case, of only six or twelve lectures. An
unwanted but unavoidable consequence of brevity is
that I have had to present many logical notions in a
way which the more advanced student will regard as
misleadingly simplified. This need not have harmful
effects if it is constantly kept in mind by the reader and
if reference is made to more advanced books whenever puzzlement supervenes.

I have been mainly concerned with purely logical conceptions but in the course of the book I have given notice of some of the major problems in the philosophy of science. I have made no attempt to solve any of these problems and few attempts even to clarify them, since this is something which demands more space than I have and which many lecturers will prefer to do for themselves in their own way.

I am grateful to Father Laurence Bright, O.P. and Drs. Mary Hesse, Michael Hoskin and Peter Nidditch for their helpful suggestions and comments. I have accepted most of their advice and rejected none of it without misgivings.

Bristol, 1961-2.   **P. A.**

THE NATURE OF THE SUBJECT

It would simplify matters if I could begin with a concise and accurate definition of the philosophy of science. But, apart from the fact that concise definitions of subjects are seldom accurate and so are likely to need modifying as the study proceeds, there are special difficulties attached to any attempt to make such a beginning in the philosophy of science or, indeed, in any branch of philosophy.

Pointing out that the philosophy of science cannot be defined in a sentence or two which will be acceptable to all philosophers of science is, in fact, taking the first step in exhibiting the nature of the subject. It is a peculiarity of philosophy, in general, that competent philosophers may disagree about the way in which their subject is to be described and about precisely what activities are to be included in it. This does not show that the subject is in a chaotic state but it does show something about the kind of subject philosophy is. This is so partly because the way in which one conceives philosophy depends upon the philosophical conclusions one has reached. A philosopher is primarily an asker of questions; only by looking back over the ground he has covered, that is, the kind of question he has considered and the kind of answer he has entertained or given, can he decide how to describe his activity.

In this respect, of course, philosophy is like science. People did not set out on scientific investigation by first deciding what science was and then proceeding to ask the questions and use the methods appropriate to this conception. Rather, their conception of science developed as they discovered ways of dealing with the questions in which they were interested.

In another respect, philosophy appears, at first sight at least, to be unlike science. On looking back over the history of philosophy one finds considerably less agreement about methods, aims and conclusions than is shown in the history of science. Philosophy tends to be greatly concerned with judgement and appraisal, with the weighing of arguments and reasons for and against particular conclusions. Matters of opinion and interpretation enter very largely into most branches of philosophy, which, in consequence, appear to be closer to literary criticism than to mathematics or physics. But it must be emphasized that an essential feature of philosophical interpretation and opinion is that they must be supported by reasons; anyone who regards himself as a philosopher must be prepared to defend his philosophical views in a reasonable way. Whether this enables us to draw a sharp line between philosophy and literary criticism is no doubt a matter of controversy.

There are, however, reservations to be made about the contentions of the last paragraph. On the one hand, close attention to the history of science suggests that science is, in respect of the firmness of its conclusions and the importance of interpretation and opinion, more like philosophy than it is popularly supposed to be. On the other hand, in formal logic, which is sometimes regarded as a branch of philosophy, opinions are of less importance than in other branches and there is a considerable range of agreed conclusions. The complication here is that formal logic may be pursued as an abstract study or as an aid to the discussion of philosophical problems; as an abstract study it resembles pure mathematics, as an adjunct to philosophy it is closer to literary criticism.

Although in most branches of philosophy there are few agreed conclusions, it is possible to find a certain amount of agreement about the kinds of problem which the various conclusions are intended to solve. It is easier to point to the characteristics of philosophical problems than it is to point to the characteristics of philosophical conclusions. This will not issue in a definition of philosophy and it carries with it the disadvantage that the nature even of philosophical problems is not fully understandable until one has gone some way into the study of philosophy. Perhaps the best approach is to consider some of the problems which have worried philosophers and with which other fields of study are not especially equipped to deal and hope that in the course of this consideration the nature of philosophy will gradually be illuminated. In other words, it is easier to show what philosophy is by carrying on discussions of philosophical problems than by talking generally *about* philosophy. Deciding what philosophy is itself involves philosophical problems.

The beginner might wonder, if this is so, how it is possible to get into the study of philosophy. How can we start doing something when we cannot know what it is we are supposed to be doing until we have done it? The situation is not as hopeless as it sounds, because some of the most important philosophical problems occur to most of us in the course of our everyday activities; anyone who asks what philosophy is, is likely to have been faced, with greater or lesser urgency, with some philosophical problems long before he came to the point of asking this question or deciding to study philosophy. Part of the business of philosophy is to discover the nature of questions which worry most of us and some likely ways of solving them. Philosophizing is partly attempting to examine these worries systematically rather than leaving them as vague and mysterious perplexities.

Perhaps the problems which most usually occur to the non-philosopher in everyday life are moral problems. When we have settled to our own satisfaction roughly which sorts of action we regard as right or wrong we may begin to wonder whether we have separated actions into these two groups on the basis of some general principle and, if so, what it is. This is not so much a question about actions as a question about the basis of our judgements about actions.

THE NATURE OF THE SUBJECT

Alternatively, it may be conceived as a question about the meanings of the terms, for example, "right" and "wrong", which we use in judging actions, rather than as a question about the kinds of action to which we are to apply these terms. In the ordinary way, an appreciation of principles is not necessarily closely associated with the ability to make moral judgements. A person may be regarded as being competent to make reliable moral judgements even if he is unable to state the principles upon which he judges. Some philosophical enquiries are aimed at making explicit any principles which are implicit in the activity in question.

Similarly, logical problems may be raised by certain everyday activities. When we are able to recognize that certain ways of reasoning are acceptable or *valid* while others are unacceptable or *invalid* we may begin to wonder about the principle or principles upon which we make this distinction, about the features of various pieces of reasoning which lead us to group them in this way. Again, this may be regarded as a question about the meanings of certain terms, such as "valid" and "invalid", which we use, not in arguing, but in criticizing arguments. If we can distinguish between valid and invalid arguments there is a sense in which we know what these terms mean even if we are unable to *state* what they mean. One of the aims of the logician is to state what is generally accepted but not stated in our everyday uses of various ways of reasoning.

In this way, we may begin to wonder about philosophical problems whatever our everyday pursuits
involve. They may arise for us out of our scientific
enquiries, our religious observances, our reading of
novels, our games, our illnesses or our hobbies. Many
philosophical questions concern the justification of
beliefs which we all hold and which, in the ordinary
way, we do not regard as either doubtful or irrational.
Very often, when the philosopher appears to be asking
questions to which the plain man knows the answer,
the philosopher is not indulging in perverse scepticism
or creating problems where none exist. This is an
appearance which depends upon a misunderstanding
of the nature of his questions.

For example, if a philosopher asks, "What right
have we to assert that such things as tables and chairs
exist?" he is not usually asking a rhetorical question
intended to cast doubt on the belief in the existence of
chairs and tables which we all, including himself,
accept. He is asking not whether the belief is true but
what justifies it, what is the evidence for its truth, by
what *right* we assert such things. He may also be trying
to discover what we mean by "exist" when we assert
that such different things as tables, stars, rainbows,
ideas and democracy *exist*. He is asking not so much
about the *correctness* of our beliefs and judgements as
about their basis and justification. He does not seek to
cast doubt upon, or correct, the views of the scientist,
the art critic, the politician, the theologian or the plain
man but simply to enquire into the possible bases and

justifications for their views; to make explicit the principles they implicitly employ; to compare and contrast their methods of reasoning in reaching their conclusions.

We may distinguish between "first-order" activities and "second-order" activities. Our daily lives are largely constituted by first-order activities but there are second-order activities in which we may engage and which spring from the first-order ones. Asking what makes plants grow is asking a first-order question but asking what sort of a question this is, e.g., whether it is a scientific or a theological question, is asking a second-order question. Helping to run a democracy is a first-order activity but considering why we should do this, rather than helping to run a dictatorship, is a second-order activity. Second-order activities depend upon first-order activities.

Asking, and attempting to answer, philosophical questions is a second-order activity in contrast to all those first-order activities which fill our daily lives. Skill in pursuing this second-order activity neither implies, nor is implied by, skill in pursuing first-order activities. The philosopher's aim is primarily to achieve *understanding* of the first-order activity in question. Whereas the plain man, the scientist and the theologian, each in his own way, seeks to understand certain aspects of the world, the philosopher seeks to understand the activities of the plain man, the scientist and the theologian and, in particular, to understand their beliefs, their interests and their reasonings. The plain man, the scientist and the theologian are not necessarily fitted, by the techniques needed for their everyday pursuits, for the understanding of those everyday pursuits; their techniques have been developed for different purposes and the philosopher must develop special techniques for *his* purposes. Philosophical problems, that is, will not yield to scientific or theological treatment or, indeed, to any but philosophical treatment.

The aim of the philosophy of science is not to advance our scientific knowledge of the world but to increase our understanding of some of the activities in which the scientist engages when he advances our scientific knowledge of the world. The philosopher seeks to do this by examining the kinds of reasoning the scientist uses, the principles and assumptions upon which he works and the aims he has when he predicts, theorizes, describes and explains. Much of this involves the logical analysis of methods, concepts and theories and the exhibiting of the logical relations between evidence and conclusions.

An example of a philosophical problem raised by contemporary biological studies will help to illustrate the relations between philosophical and scientific problems. It has been found that viruses, under certain conditions, exhibit characteristics which would incline us to say that they are living organisms and under other conditions exhibit characteristics which would incline us to deny this. For example, they grow, take in nourishment and reproduce themselves, but they can be separated into constituent parts which do not exhibit these characteristics. Further, the parts can be refrigerated for long periods and again combined to reproduce a virus which behaves like a living organism. The question arises, "Are viruses living or non-living?"

This question is one for the philosophy of science rather than for science, for several reasons. The scientist is not hampered in his investigation of the characteristics and behaviour of viruses by his inability to answer this question. He can discover whether a virus has the property *a*, *b* or *c*, and so can learn how to manipulate viruses, without having to decide whether it is living or not. The scientific question concerns what *properties* viruses have and life is not a property in the sense in which the ability to reproduce is a property. The philosophical question concerns how we are to classify or describe viruses, given that they have just those properties the biologist has discovered. To say that a virus is living, or non-living, is not to attribute to it a scientifically discoverable property, but to classify it in a certain way on the basis of its scientifically discoverable properties. The question is not, "Do viruses have the (scientifically discoverable) properties *a*, *b* or *c* and life?" but rather "Does the fact that viruses have the properties *a*, *b*, *c* justify our classifying them along with living things?"

It may even be that, as a result of the scientific findings that viruses persistently exhibit characteristics which incline us to say both that they are living and that they are non-living, we may be led to maintain that our two terms "living" and "non-living" do not, after all, represent classes between which we can draw a sharp line. It may be that, at the borderline, if it is important to answer the philosophical question, we just have to make a more or less arbitrary decision about where to draw the line between the living and the non-living. That is, it is a case not for scientific discovery but for reasonable decision. The philosophical question is not an empirical question which further scientific evidence will answer but a question of what we *mean* by "living" and "non-living" in view of the way in which we use these terms in classifying things. If the present question is not readily answered by an examination of the way in which we have previously used these terms, this may be because it has not been necessary so far to define them closely enough for this present situation. Then what is called for is a decision about what we propose to mean by these terms in future.

This is a question about the implications of certain scientific conclusions, and many questions in the philosophy of science are of this sort. We can ask, for example, whether the scientific account of colour vision entitles us to say that the familiar objects of our daily experience are not, after all, really coloured; whether the atomic theory entitles us to say that tables and billiard balls are not really hard; whether the deterministic account of human behaviour towards which physiological investigation appears to be leading entitles us to say that human beings are never able to choose freely between two courses of action. These are not questions which could be answered by further scientific investigation, since they involve questions about the meanings of such terms as "really coloured", "really hard", "deterministic" and "freely". Moreover, they involve the questioning of assumptions which the scientist makes and without which his conclusions would not be as they are. For example, the scientific account of colour vision purports to be an account of what occurs *when we see a coloured object*, so it would be odd and self-contradictory to conclude that what occurs is that we don't see a coloured object. We might conclude this on other grounds but not on grounds which involve the assumption of its denial.

Questions about these large implications of scientific conclusions are no doubt the sort of philosophical questions which are most likely to interest the non-philosopher, at least in the first place. But many philosophers of science spend most of their time on apparently more pedestrian sorts of question. These primarily concern methods of reasoning in the sciences and the logical relations holding between various kinds of scientific statements. We can ask, for example, whether there are distinctions to be drawn between the logical principles underlying the reasoning used in pure mathematics and those underlying the reasoning in the observational sciences such as astronomy, physics and botany; and whether the methods of these sciences can give final certainty or only probable and provisional conclusions. We can attempt to give a clear account of the role of observation and of the exact function of hypotheses about unobservable entities, such as are apparently used in many scientific theories. We can consider whether it is necessary or useful to distinguish between hypotheses, laws and theories and, if so, how the distinctions are to be drawn. We can ask how hypotheses are formed and how laws and theories are established; we can seek to exhibit the logical structure of theories.

These questions lead us on to, or spring from, more general questions about the nature of science. Is the aim and function of the sciences to explain or can they do no more than describe? How do explanation and description differ? How do explanations work in the various fields in which we are concerned to explain? Does the scientist depend upon certain very general presuppositions about the world—for example, the presupposition that every event has a discoverable cause? If so, do such presuppositions enter into his reasoning as logical principles or do they merely amount to beliefs which keep him going and without which he would have no stimulus for continued investigation?

These philosophical questions, like the question whether viruses are living or non-living, are not questions which the working scientist must answer before he can proceed. They are directed towards the improvement of our understanding of what is involved in scientific reasoning rather than towards the improvement of that reasoning. Although my catalogue is far from complete, it gives some indication of the scope of the philosophy of science and it brings out the fact that the central question is, "What is science?" This question is asked in a particular spirit; of course, in one sense we all know the answer to it, for we can all point to certain activities and say, "These are sciences." In the context of the philosophy of science the question is to be understood as a request for an account of the features of these activities which lead us to classify them together in this way and to distinguish them from other activities.

The question, "What is science?", is always of theoretical importance to anyone who wishes to understand the classifications we use; it is of practical importance if we wish to decide, as we sometimes do, whether a particular study is to be regarded as scientific. Is astrology a science? Is psychology a science? What is it that inclines us to answer "No" to the first question and "Yes" to the second? Deciding this involves a comparison of the methods and conclusions of astrology and psychology with one another and with the methods and conclusions of those activities which we unhesitatingly regard as sciences, and this in turn involves such considerations as I have mentioned.

The philosophy of science has often, in the past, been referred to as "scientific method" and "inductive logic". Both titles are misleading because they are too narrow and, more seriously, because they beg some important questions. The first suggests that there is only one method common to all branches of science and to all fields within each branch; the second suggests that there is one kind of reasoning, inductive reasoning, which is central and fundamental to all scientific investigations. But both these suggestions themselves involve questions for the philosophy of science and both would nowadays be rejected by many reputable philosophers of science.

It should be clear from what I have said so far that a study of the history of science may be a valuable aid to the solving of problems in the philosophy of science. By examining the ways in which particular conclusions have been arrived at we may discover something about the weight given by scientists to various ways of supporting them. By examining out-of-date theories we may discover something about the reasons for which theories are rejected or modified. By examining outworn concepts we may discover something about the reasons for replacing them and so come to a clearer understanding of the new concepts. In general, historical studies may help us to keep our logical account in harmony with the actual practice of scientists. However, the historical approach can be overdone and may lead us, by confining our attention to actual procedures and the fortuitous features of particular discoveries, to confuse the psychology of discovery and the history of science with the philosophy of science.

The philosophy of science is concerned with the ways in which scientific conclusions are, or may be, supported and justified rather than the ways in which they are arrived at. This latter concern may be interesting and valuable but it lies within the fields of the historian and the psychologist rather than the philosopher. He is less interested in the shrewd guesswork of Einstein and the mysticism of Kepler than in the reasons which justify the acceptance and retention of their results by reasonable men who may be bad guessers or indifferent mystics. It would perhaps be less misleading to regard those aspects of the philosophy of science with which I have been mainly dealing as the *logic of science*.

Those who are mainly interested in this aspect are frequently accused, by both scientists and philosophers, of giving accounts of the sciences which are not faithful pictures of the way in which the scientist in fact works. This accusation results from a failure to understand what the logician of science is attempting to do. A logical analysis of a method need not look like a description of that method, or a recipe for doing something, any more than a critic's comments on the merits of a painting need look like an account either of the artist's behaviour while painting it or of the factors which led him to paint it as he did. We should expect an analytical chemist's report on a cake to look rather different from a cook's recipe for making it and we should not dismiss his report as inaccurate because the cook failed to recognize in it an account of what he did in making the cake. Just because the logician is interested in unstated assumptions made by the scientist and in the clarification of meanings which the scientist does not need, in his practice, to clarify, we should be surprised if the logician *did* produce an account which looked like a straight-forward description of the scientist's procedures.

In the following sections I have the very limited aim of explaining some of the logical conceptions which most philosophers of science use in their exploration of the logic of the sciences and of the wider problems concerning the implications of scientific conclusions. Many of these conceptions can be sufficiently understood without an appreciation of the full apparatus of the formal logician, although it must be stressed that such an appreciation is not to be scorned. I shall, therefore, refer to some standard textbooks of logic where more detailed discussions of these matters may be found. What I have to say, here, is almost entirely prefatory to the philosophy of science and to the full understanding of the questions which philosophers of science discuss.

2

TYPES OF STATEMENT

A sentence in a given language is a collection of words arranged in such a way as to obey the grammatical and syntactical rules of that language. In most languages there are different kinds of sentences which may be used for various purposes. The following are examples of English sentences.

    (a) Gorillas are fierce.
    (b) Gazelles are not fierce.
    (c) This is a gorilla.
    (d) Is that a gazelle?
    (e) Keep away from the gorilla.

The first three sentences may be used to make *statements*, the fourth to ask a question and the fifth to issue a command or a warning. I have not used the sentences for these purposes for I have not intended to make statements, ask questions or issue commands about gazelles or gorillas; I have merely mentioned these sentences as examples. According to the view I am adopting, a sentence is a mere collection of words satisfying certain conditions, but some sentences may be used on particular occasions to make statements, that is, to state or assert that something is the case. It is only statements which can be true or false, for it is only when something is asserted that there is anything to be true or false. For the sake of brevity, I shall sometimes refer to sentences as "statements" and it should be borne in mind that what is then being discussed is the statements which those sentences are, or may be, used to make.

There are relations between statements which depend upon certain formal or structural characteristics of the statements themselves and an important part of logic is the study of these relations. In this section I shall mention some of the more important of these formal characteristics.

A statement is an assertion that something is the case and statements may be distinguished according to whether the assertions are made with reservations or not and, if so, according to the kind of reservation involved. Traditionally, a broad distinction has been drawn between *categorical* and *conditional* statements. According to this classification, statements are categorical if they assert something without reservations, that is, unconditionally, and conditional if they assert that something is the case with reservations, that is, under certain conditions. Thus the statement

(1) Gorillas are fierce

is categorical, whereas the statement

(2) If gorillas are hungry then they are fierce

and the statement

(3) Either gorillas are not hungry or they are fierce

are both conditional.

Within this classification, statement (2), and any statement of the form "If (. . .) then (_ _ _)", where (. . .) and (_ _ _) stand for complete indicative sentences, are further classified as *hypothetical*; statement (3), and any statement of the form "Either (. . .) or (_ _ _)", where (. . .) and (_ _ _) stand for complete indicative sentences, are further classified as *disjunctive*.

There are, however, disadvantages attached to this classification which have justified its modification. I shall mention what seem to me to be the two chief disadvantages. The first concerns the use of the label "conditional" for hypothetical and disjunctive statements; the second concerns the use of the label "disjunctive" for all statements of the form "Either (. . .) or (_ _ _)". I shall deal with these in turn.

Although statements (2) and (3) may be regarded as asserting that gorillas are fierce *under certain conditions*, they may also be regarded as asserting *unconditionally* something quite different. For logical purposes it is often necessary to regard them in this way. Thus, (2) asserts unconditionally that a certain relation holds between its two component statements, "gorillas are hungry" and "they (gorillas) are fierce"; it asserts that the second is true whenever the first is true and that the first is true only when the second is true, that is, that the truth or falsity of the component statements is linked in a particular way. Similarly (3) asserts that another relation holds between its component statements; it asserts that one or the other is true, that is, that the truth or falsity of either depends in a particular way on the truth or falsity of the other.

This leads me to the second difficulty I have mentioned. The use of the term "disjunctive" for all statements of the form "Either (...) or (_ _ _)" obscures the fact that there are two kinds of statement of this general form. Compare the statements

(3) Either gorillas are not hungry or they are fierce

and

(4) Either gorillas are stupid or they are lazy.

Both statements involve the assertion that one or other of their components is true. We might conclude from (3) that we are unlikely to meet a gorilla which is both not hungry and fierce whereas (4) does not so strongly suggest that we are unlikely to meet a gorilla which is both stupid and lazy. In fact, we may use "either ... or ..." to make a compound statement in such a way that one of its components must be true and both may be; this is called the "*inclusive*" use of "either ... or ...". On the other hand we may use "either ... or ..." in such a way that one of the components must be true and both cannot be; this is called the "*exclusive*" use of "either ... or ...". It is usual nowadays to classify statements of the form "Either (...) or (_ _ _)" as *disjunctive* when the "either ... or ..." is inclusive and as *alternative* when the "either ... or ..." is exclusive. If nothing to the contrary is said, "either ... or ..." is taken to be inclusive.

It is, therefore, better, and nowadays more usual, to classify statements of the forms (1), (2), (3) and (4) as, respectively, *categorical*, *hypothetical*, *alternative* and *disjunctive* and to drop the label "conditional" for statements of the forms (2), (3) and (4). These descriptions draw our attention more clearly to the kind of assertion being made. It is important, however, to bear in mind that this is not the only system of nomenclature in use.

In the examples I have been citing, according to the interpretation I have adopted, (1) is a factual statement or, more precisely, may be used to assert that something is true of the world, while (2), (3) and (4) may be used to assert unconditionally, that something is true of the relation between their component statements and only conditionally that something is true of the world. However, categorical statements need not be factual, in the sense that they are about the world. For example, it is often held that mathematical statements such as

> Things equal to the same thing are equal to one another

or

$$2+2 = 4,$$

while categorical, are not about the world but about, respectively, certain concepts and a part of the number system we habitually use. Similarly the statement

> If $2+2 = 4$ and $3+1 = 4$ then $2+2 = 3+1$

expresses a relation between statements which are

about a part of that system and is hypothetical. I shall return to this later.

Categorical statements have traditionally been further distinguished from one another according to the breadth of the assertions made; they may be *universal, particular* or *singular*. The two statements

> All gorillas are fierce

and

> No gorillas are fierce

differ in that the first is affirmative and the second negative; they are alike in that they both assert something of the whole class named by the *subject* term, "gorillas", and so are both *universal*. If this is not obviously true of the negative statement, it is clearer when we realize that this statement is equivalent to the statement

> All gorillas are non-fierce.

The two statements

> Some gorillas are fierce

and

> Some gorillas are not fierce

are both *particular* because they are both about only part of the class named by the subject term.

The two statements

> This gorilla is fierce

and

> King Richard III of England was fierce

are both *singular* because each is about an individual who is, in some sense, unique. The first is singular because, presumably, only one gorilla is at the moment being pointed at and so indicated by "this", and the second because only one man *can* correctly be indicated by the title "King Richard III of England".

Singular statements have, for certain logical purposes, been treated as universal statements, for both kinds of statement have been regarded as asserting something about a whole class and not merely about part of a class. The terms "This gorilla" and "King Richard III of England" are regarded, on this interpretation, as naming classes each of which has only one member.

The classification adopted in this section may now be summarized and generalized. If we represent terms by the capital letters *A* and *B*, unique individuals by *a*, and categorical statements by *p* and *q*, we can symbolize the various types of statement in the following way:

(i) Categorical
    (a) Universal   (1) Affirmative All *A* is *B*
                 (2) Negative   No *A* is *B*
    (b) Particular (1) Affirmative Some *A* is *B*
                 (2) Negative   Some *A* is not *B*
    (c) Singular   (1) Affirmative *a* is *B* (*or* This *A* is *B*)
                 (2) Negative   *a* is not *B* (or This *A* is not *B*)
(ii) Hypothetical   If *p* then *q*
(iii) Disjunctive   Either *p* or *q* (and possibly both)
(iv) Alternative   Either *p* or *q* (but not both)

In the categorical statements *A* represents the *subject* term and *B* the *predicate* term. In hypothetical statements *p* represents the *antecedent* and *q* the *consequent*. In disjunctive statements *p* and *q* are *disjuncts* and in alternative statements *alternates*.

It must now be noted that the examples of categorical statements I have used are all of a type which attributes a property to something. These are sometimes called *predicative* statements. There are, however, other kinds of categorical statements which sometimes have to be treated differently from the logical point of view. Consider, first, the statement

> Gorillas are fiercer than gazelles

It would be odd to regard this as a statement which attributes the property *fiercer than gazelles* to gorillas in the way in which the statement

> Gorillas are fierce

attributes the property *fierce* to gorillas. It is better to distinguish these as different types of statement and to regard

Gorillas are fiercer than gazelles

as asserting a relation between two kinds of thing, gorillas and gazelles. Thus, statements of this kind are sometimes called *relational* statements, and represented, for some purposes at least, by the formula

$$A R B$$

where *A* and *B* stand for the terms, here, "gorillas"

and "gazelles" and R for the relating expression, here, *are fiercer than*.

Again, consider the statement

Congo is a gorilla

Here, it is said, *gorilla* is not a property which is being attributed to Congo; rather it is a class of things of which Congo is said to be a member. Such statements are, therefore, sometimes called *class-membership* statements.

However, there are complexities and uncertainties in this region. There is disagreement about the relations between predicative, relational and class-membership statements and about the relations of all these to statements which assert that one class of things is included in another. It would not be appropriate to enter into these disagreements now; it is sufficient to draw attention to some of the points involved and to mention that the notion of predication is by no means a simple one.

3

RELATIONS BETWEEN STATEMENTS

I propose next to explain some of the relations which hold between statements of the kinds I have so far mentioned. These relations determine the ways in which we may move from one statement to another, that is, the inferences we may make.

First, consider the relations between a universal affirmative statement and a particular affirmative statement of the same form, that is, between a statement of the form

All *A* is *B*,

and a statement of the form

Some *A* is *B*

where *A* and *B*, respectively, stand for the same terms in each statement. It is clear that the truth of the particular statement does not imply the truth of the universal statement but that if the particular statement is false the universal statement must be false also. It does not follow from the fact that six gorillas in the London Zoo are fierce that all gorillas are fierce. But if six gorillas in the London Zoo are not fierce then it cannot be true that *all* gorillas are fierce.

On the face of it, it seems equally clear that we can

say, quite generally, that if the universal statement is true, then the particular statement must also be true. If all gorillas are fierce it seems to follow that the gorillas in the London Zoo must be fierce. There are, however, difficulties about this because, it is said, a universal statement may be true even if its subject term has no instances whereas a particular statement cannot.

For example, the statement

Some men are dishonest

can be true only if there *are* men among whom we can distinguish those who are honest and those who are dishonest. If there were no men this statement would not be merely false; it would not even be sensible, since its whole point is to distinguish between two sorts of men.

On the other hand, suppose I imagine an animal which I call a "snurb". Since this is my invention I am entitled to say what characteristics an actual animal must have in order for it to be correctly called "a snurb" or what characteristics an animal which I called "a snurb" would have if it existed. For example, I am entitled to say

All snurbs have webbed feet and bushy tails

and it makes sense to say that this is meaningful and true, even if there are no snurbs, because I have given it meaning and made it true. My statement is, if you like, part of a definition.

However, since there are no snurbs, I am not entitled to say that

> Some snurbs are pink

because, it is said, this implies that there *are* snurbs among which I can distinguish some that are pink and some that are not.

This can be put in another way. The point of my universal statement can be caught by expressing it in a hypothetical form, thus

> If anything is a snurb then it has webbed feet and a bushy tail

but I cannot express the particular statement in a hypothetical form. It does not mean the same as

> If anything is a snurb then it is pink

nor does it mean the same as

> If anything is a snurb then it may be pink

or, indeed, any other hypothetical statement. In general, it is said, a universal statement of the form

> All *A* is *B*

can be expressed in the form

> If anything is an *A* then it is a *B*,

but a particular statement of the form

> Some *A* is *B*

cannot, and must be put in the form

> There are *A*'s and some of them are *B*.

Yet another way of bringing this out is to say that the point of a universal statement is that it *excludes* a certain possibility. That is, a statement of the form

All *A* is *B*

excludes the possibility of an *A* that is not *B* and so is equivalent to

Nothing is both *A* and not *B*,

whereas

Some *A* is *B*

is equivalent to

Something is both *A* and *B*.

Similarly, for negative statements, the universal

No *A* is *B*

is equivalent to

Nothing is both *A* and *B*

whereas the particular statement

Some *A* is not *B*

is equivalent to

Something is both *A* and not *B*.

We can express this in the language of classes. The statement

All gorillas are fierce

may be regarded as a statement about a relation

between two classes of things, the class of *gorillas* and the class of *fierce animals*. Similarly, the statement

All snurbs have webbed feet

may be regarded as referring to the class of *snurbs* and the class of *animals with webbed feet*. The important difference is that the class of gorillas has members, that is, there *are* gorillas, while the class of snurbs has no members, that is, there are no snurbs. A class with no members is an *empty class*. However, this difference is not implicit in the two universal statements; we depend on knowledge we have independently of these.

If all this is so, then a universal categorical statement cannot imply the corresponding particular statement, since the particular statement involves an assertion of the existence of something, whereas the universal statement does not. We always require, along with the universal statement, another statement asserting the existence of members of the class named by the subject term.

It must be said, however, that in a given situation it is usually clear from the context whether existence is being presupposed when a universal categorical statement is made. If it is not being presupposed it would seem to be correct to say that the corresponding particular statement is not implied. On the other hand, if it is being presupposed we may say that the particular is implied by the universal without any additional statement about existence because it is clear from the context that the universal is being taken to involve an assertion of existence. In fact, we cannot make a general rule either about the existential implications of universal statements or, in consequence, about their relation to particular statements. In other words, this is not a purely formal matter but depends partly on context.

We sometimes use the word "contradiction", and related words, loosely to indicate any kind of conflict or inconsistency between two statements. The logician uses this word in a technical sense and distinguishes between *contradiction* and *contrariety*. Thus, the two statements

> All trees are green

and

> Some trees are not green

are, according to this use, contradictory statements.

The relations which determine this are that the statements can neither be true at the same time nor false at the same time. In other words, if either is false the other must be true and if either is true the other must be false. The same relations hold between the statements

> No trees are green

and

> Some trees are green.

On the other hand, the two statements

All trees are green

and

No trees are green

are contrary statements. The relations which determine this are that the statements cannot be true at the same time but they may both be false. When this is so, the statement

Some trees are green and some are not green

is true.

The difference between contradictory statements and contrary statements is that a pair of contradictory statements exhausts the possibilities while a pair of contrary statements does not; between contraries there is a third possibility when both are false. Thus contradictories may be said to be in "stronger" opposition to one another than contraries. This is important in argument, since we may support a statement more effectively by disproving its contradictory than by disproving its contrary.

What I have been saying about contradiction and contrariety may be put more generally. Any two statements of the forms

All *A* is *B*

and

Some *A* is not *B*

or

No *A* is *B*

and

> Some *A* is *B*

are contradictory to one another, whereas any two statements of the forms

> All *A* is *B*

and

> No *A* is *B*

are contrary to one another. Even more generally, we may say that *any* two statements, of whatever forms, which are so related that one must be true and the other false and that they cannot be either true or false at the same time, are contradictories; and that *any* two statements, of whatever forms, which are so related that they cannot be true at the same time but may be false at the same time, are contraries.

It should be obvious that the distinctions I have noted between categorical, hypothetical, disjunctive and alternative statements do not represent rigid, uncrossable barriers. If we ignore special uses, that is, ignore contexts and consider only the forms of the statements, alone, we can see that it is possible to lay down general rules for transforming statements from one of these forms into the others. For example, a categorical statement may be transformed into a disjunctive statement without change of meaning.

If the statement

> All gorillas are fierce

is true, then it is also true that

If x is a gorilla then x is fierce

and that

Either x is not a gorilla or x is fierce,

where x stands for the name of any object.

If this is not immediately obvious, a little consideration will make it so; it will also make it clear that the transformation can be made in the opposite direction.

Various transformations are also possible with the help of negation. Among the most important is the transformation of

If x is a gorilla then x is fierce

into

If x is not fierce then x is not a gorilla

and, correspondingly, of

All gorillas are fierce

into

All non-fierce animals are non-gorillas.

Clearly if anything that is a gorilla is fierce, anything that is not fierce, for that reason alone, cannot be a gorilla.

Our consideration of contradiction and contrariety concerned the simplest examples of the relations between a statement and its denial. More complex are the relations between compound statements and their denials.

Simple categorical statements, represented by p, q, r, s, etc., may be compounded notably by joining them with "or" and "and", to obtain statements of the forms

(1) p or q or r or s

and

(2) p and q and r and s.

The truth of these compounds depends upon the truth of their simple categorical components, in the following way. Statement (1) is true if at least one of its components p, q, r and s is true. If the "or" is used inclusively, (1) is still true even if *all* the components are true. Statement (2) is true if and only if all the components, p, q, r and s, are true. These, of course, are simply consequences of the meanings of the words "or" and "and".

Now, these compound statements may be denied by someone who says "No, that's not true." That is, in place of (1) he will be making another compound statement which can be represented by

(3) Not (p or q or r or s).

Then, if the inclusive "or" is being used (3) can be true only when all the components are false, that is, when the statement

(4) Not p and not q and not r and not s

is true. If the exclusive "or" is being used (3) can be true under two conditions, first, when (4) is true and, second, when *all* the components are true, that is, when the statement

(5) *p* and *q* and *r* and *s*

is true.

The denial of (2) amounts to the assertion of

(6) Not (*p* and *q* and *r* and *s*),

and since (2) is true only if *p*, *q*, *r* and *s* are all individually true, the falsity of one of these is sufficient to ensure the falsity of (2) and therefore the truth of (6). Thus, (6) can be true only if

(7) Not *p* or not *q* or not *r* or not *s*

is true, where "or" is used inclusively.

Thus anyone who denies (1) is asserting either (4) or (5) and anyone who denies (2) is asserting (7).

The denial of hypothetical statements is also of some importance. One who denies

If gorillas are hungry then they are fierce

is asserting that gorillas are not fierce even when they are hungry, that is,

If gorillas are hungry then they are not fierce.

He cannot be asserting that

If gorillas are not hungry then they are fierce

or that

If gorillas are not hungry then they are not fierce

for to assert either of these is not to deny the original statement; the original statement does not rule out the possibility that gorillas are fierce all the time or the possibility that they are not fierce when not hungry.

We may generalize this. The denial of any statement of the form

If p then q

amounts to the assertion of a statement of the form

If p then not q.

SOME PROPERTIES OF RELATIONS

The relations between statements are sometimes determined by relations within those statements. For example, the fact that the two statements

4 is greater than 3

and

3 is greater than 2

together imply the statement

4 is greater than 2

depends upon the relation "is greater than". Every relation, whether it holds between statements or within statements, has certain logical properties which determine how it functions and what we can do with it. These properties do not depend upon the terms related; they belong to the relations whatever terms they are used to relate. For example, it is because of certain logical properties of the relation "is greater than" (symbolized by " > ") that we are able to argue not only that

$$\text{If} \quad 4 > 3$$
$$\text{and} \quad 3 > 2$$
$$\text{then} \quad 4 > 2$$

but also

$$\begin{aligned} &\text{If} & a &> b \\ &\text{and} & b &> c \\ &\text{then} & a &> c, \end{aligned}$$

where all we know about *a*, *b* and *c* is that they stand for appropriate terms. We are able, that is, to say that a relation holds between three statements *not* because of something we know about numbers but because of something we know about the relation "is greater than", which each statement contains. I shall here deal with only some of the logical properties of relations.

We may represent relations which hold between two terms by

$$x \, R \, y$$

where *x* and *y* stand for the terms and *R* for the relation between them. Now any such relation is, (A), either *symmetrical*, *asymmetrical* or *non-symmetrical* and, also, (B), either *transitive*, *intransitive* or *non-transitive*. I shall explain these in turn.

(A) (1) *Symmetrical:* A relation, *R*, is symmetrical if it follows from $x \, R \, y$ that $y \, R \, x$. For example, *is equal to* is a symmetrical relation since $x = y$ entails $y = x$.

(2) *Asymmetrical:* A relation, *R*, is asymmetrical if $x \, R \, y$ is incompatible with $y \, R \, x$. For example, *is greater than* is an asymmetrical relation, since if *x* is greater than *y* then *y* cannot be greater than *x*.

(3) *Non-symmetrical:* A relation *R* is non-symmetrical if $x \, R \, y$ neither entails nor is incompatible with $y \, R \, x$. That is, if $x \, R \, y$ then possibly $y \, R \, x$ and possibly not. For example, *is a sister of* is a non-symmetrical relation since, if *x* is a sister of *y*

then y may be either a sister of x or a brother of x.

(B) (1) *Transitive :* A relation, R, is transitive if it follows from $x R y$ and $y R z$, together, that $x R z$. For example, *is greater than* is a transitive relation, as we have already seen.

(2) *Intransitive :* A relation, R, is intransitive if $x R y$ and $y R z$, together, are incompatible with $x R z$. For example, *is the father of* is intransitive, since if Paul is the father of Hubert and Hubert is the father of Michael, then Paul cannot be the father of Michael.

(3) *Non-transitive :* A relation, R, is non-transitive if $x R y$ and $y R z$, together, neither entail nor are incompatible with $x R z$. For example, *is different from* is a non-transitive relation since two things may differ in a certain respect from a third thing and either differ or not differ in that respect from one another.

Now, every relation between two terms has one property from group A and one from group B. We can see that if we take every possible combination of a property from group A with a property from group B, there are nine kinds of relation. Some of these are more important than others, for logical purposes. Examples from among the most important are *is equal to*, a symmetrical transitive relation, *is greater than*, an asymmetrical transitive relation, and *is greater by one than*, an asymmetrical intransitive relation.

Relations may hold between terms of various logical categories, for example, between physical objects (e.g., *is larger than*), between words (e.g., *means the same as*), between numbers or complex mathematical expressions (e.g., *is equal to*), between statements (e.g., *is equivalent to*), and so on. Perhaps the most important relation for our purpose is *implies*, the relation of *implication*, holding between statements. This is a non-symmetrical transitive relation, since if p implies q then q may or may not imply p and if p implies q and q implies r then p implies r. What is most important about this relation is that it is *transitive*; this is an essential property of a relation which entitles us to make inferences involving more than two statements.

It is upon the transitivity of the relation involved that we rely when we infer thus:

$$(1) \quad 4 > 3$$
$$3 > 2$$
therefore $\quad 4 > 2$

and thus:

$$(2) \quad 7+3 = 10$$
$$10 = 6+4$$
therefore $\quad 7+3 = 6+4$

and thus:

(3) All cows are mammals
     All mammals are suckled in infancy
therefore All cows are suckled in infancy.

It is the transitivity of the relation which carries us forward from two statements to a third or from any number of statements, each involving a transitive relation, to a further statement.

A relation which is of great importance in inference

is the relation of *class-inclusion*. In the last inference quoted above, the word "cows" can be regarded as naming a class of which each individual cow is a member, but when we say

> All cows are mammals

we can regard ourselves as saying

> The class of cows is included in (*or* is part of) the class of mammals.

Similarly, when we say

> All mammals are suckled in infancy

we can regard ourselves as saying

> The class of mammals is included in the class of animals suckled in infancy.

The inference depends upon this relation of *class-inclusion* and, in particular, upon the fact that it is a transitive relation, for this allows us to go on to say

> The class of cows is included in the class of animals suckled in infancy,

that is,

> All cows are suckled in infancy.

It should be noted that when we say

> The class of mammals is included in the class of animals suckled in infancy

we cannot say "is part of" in place of "is included in" because *only* mammals are suckled in infancy. "Mammal" is so defined.

In general we can say that a class α is included in a class β if every member of α is a member of β. This allows the case in which α is only a part of β and the case in which α exhausts β (e.g., all mammals are suckled in infancy) but not, of course, the case in which part of α is not part of β.

Because of the transitivity of the relation of *class-inclusion* we can say that the first two statements in the inference (3), above, imply the third; if we can now go on to show that the third statement implies a fourth then, because of the transitivity of *implication*, we can say that the first two statements imply the fourth. And so on.

The relation of class-inclusion is to be distinguished from the relation of class-membership, most importantly because class-membership is non-transitive. If the class α is included in the class β and this in turn in the class γ then the class α is included in the class γ and any member of α is a member of β and a member of γ. But if John Smith is a member of the Hairsplitters' Union and the Hairsplitters' Union is a member of the Trades Union Congress, it does not follow that John Smith is a member of the Trades Union Congress. Only individual persons may be members of the Hairsplitters' Union and only trade unions can be members of the Trades Union Congress. Because of this difference between class-inclusion and class-membership, class-inclusion is far more useful for inference than class-membership.

5

PATTERNS OF REASONING: DEDUCTION

A distinction which has received considerable attention in the philosophy of science is that between *deductive* and *inductive* inference. In many textbooks of logic, mathematics has been referred to as a deductive science while the natural sciences, such as physics, chemistry and zoology, have been referred to as inductive sciences, in the belief that it is the use of different patterns of inference which chiefly determines the contrasting characteristics of these two broad fields of study. Although this distinction has recently come under fire from several directions, so much in our subject has been based upon it that it is important to know what it involves. Besides, this is still a matter of controversy and it is likely that, as so often happens in philosophical discussion, there has been a tendency for philosophers to swing from one extreme to the other while the truth lies somewhere in between.

I shall first point to some important and relevant features of deductive reasoning.

A piece of reasoning is a complex affair, but the core of it, what may be called the *argument* or the *inference*, can be captured and, as it were, fossilized

upon a page. It is from this that the logician starts.
Two such inferences are

(1) $3+2 = 5$
    $4+1 = 5$
    $\therefore 3+2 = 4+1$

and

(2) All mammals are vertebrates
    All gorillas are mammals
    $\therefore$ All gorillas are vertebrates.

These are both deductive inferences. In each, the
first two statements are the *premisses* and the third is
the *conclusion*, as is indicated by the sign for "therefore". These inferences happen to have two premisses
each but a deductive inference may have any number
of premisses. The second example is a *syllogism*.

Although these examples differ in certain respects,
what is important for our purpose is that they have
features in common which make them deductive.
Their most striking feature is that in each the conclusion *certainly follows* from the premisses, or, to say
the same thing differently, the premisses *entail* or
imply the conclusion. This means that if the premisses
are true then the conclusion must be true and this is
what is meant by saying that they are *valid* inferences.
It must be noted at once that whether the premisses
and conclusion are in fact true is irrelevant to the
validity of the inference since validity depends merely
on the *relations* between the premisses and the
conclusion. That is, a valid deductive inference is just

defined as being one in which if the premisses are (or were) true then the conclusion must be (or would necessarily be) true. It would be contradictory to assert that a deductive inference with true premisses and a false conclusion was valid.

Since saying that an inference is deductively valid is merely saying that *if* such and such is the case *then* so and so is the case, this does not amount to the assertion that so and so *is* the case. The mere fact that an inference is valid is not sufficient to establish the truth of its conclusion, that is, to prove (the truth of) its conclusion. In order to prove (the truth of) a conclusion we need not only a valid inference but also true premisses.

It is important in this connection to distinguish between *implication* and *inference*. Implication is a relation between statements upon which inferences depend; inference is strictly the movement from one statement, or set of statements, to a different statement which is regarded as implied, that is, it is the process of drawing a conclusion. Thus, implication is a relation which holds between certain statements whether or not we use it for making inferences. In making an inference we assert the truth of a statement or statements as the ground for the assertion of some other statement, but in stating an implication we assert nothing about the truth of these statements but only that this relation holds between them. Valid inferences depend upon implications but implications do not depend upon inferences.

If we are to speak strictly in accordance with the substance of the last paragraph, it follows that the examples given above are not inferences; they only represent inferences. This is connected with the fact that what is printed on the page is a group of sentences, and sentences are not statements. A sentence is a certain arrangement of words and so does not assert or state anything, although some sentences may be used by people to assert or state or to make statements. An inference is a movement from something asserted to the assertion of something else, that is, from statement to statement. It is a movement carried out by a person and it depends upon that person's using sentences to assert or make statements. For convenience, I shall continue to refer to groups of sentences representing inferences as "inferences" but the elliptical nature of this procedure must be borne in mind.

Now, when we say that an inference is valid we are saying only that the relation of implication holds between its premisses and its conclusion. Thus

      All mammals are vertebrates
      All gorillas are mammals
   ∴ All gorillas are vertebrates

is an inference because the premisses and the conclusion are asserted. What we assert may, of course, be true or false and the inference, if it is valid, will accordingly either establish or fail to establish the truth of its conclusion. If we are not concerned about, or do not wish to commit ourselves to, the truth of the premisses but we recognize that it is a valid inference, we may emphasize this by writing

> *If* all mammals are vertebrates
> *and* all gorillas are mammals
> *then* all gorillas are vertebrates.

This merely states the implication upon which the inference is based. The implication is said to *hold*. Implications are not said to be valid; they are said to account for the validity of inferences based upon them. Logicians are interested in the implications under-lying deductive inferences rather than in the inferences themselves, since it is not their aim as logicians to settle matters of truth and falsity.

A consequent feature of deductive inferences is that we can usually decide whether they are valid or invalid, although not, of course, whether their conclusions are true or false, without reference to their subject-matter. Most logicians have said that we can always do this. Their validity is a formal matter because it depends upon those relations between statements which depend on their form or structure rather than upon what the statements are about. (But see below, pp. 52-3.)

We can see this by reconsidering our specimen inferences, and representing merely the *pattern* of each, by using symbols to "eliminate" their subject matter. In this way we can see that each pattern of inference is valid whatever its subject matter. Consider again

(1) $3+2 = 5$

       $4+1 = 5$

       $\therefore 3+2 = 4+1$

We may be inclined to think that our seeing that this is valid depends upon our seeing the particular connection between these particular numbers. But we may write

(1)a $a+b = c$

        $d+e = c$

        $\therefore a+b = d+e$

and still see that the conclusion follows, whatever numbers are substituted for the letters, as long as the same number is substituted for a given letter whenever it occurs. That is, the validity of the inference depends upon the way in which we use the symbols "$+$" and "$=$" and the arrangement of the terms symbolized by a, b, c, d and e, rather than upon the particular numbers used in (1). That is, it depends upon the form of the statements rather than upon their content. The three lines of (1)a cannot be used separately to assert anything, and so could not be used to make either true or false statements. Taken together, they can be regarded as asserting that it is allowable to move from two statements to a third statement provided that these statements have the forms indicated. Thus the validity of this pattern of inference does not depend upon the truth or falsity of statements composing it.

Similarly, the pattern of the inference

(2)   All mammals are vertebrates
       All gorillas are mammals
∴ All gorillas are vertebrates

can be exhibited by eliminating its subject matter and writing

(2)*a*   All *A* is *B*
          All *C* is *A*
∴ All *C* is *B*.

We can still see that this is a valid pattern of inference, whatever terms *A*, *B* and *C* stand for.

I have dealt with only two of the possible inference patterns; there are many more, two of the most important of which are known as *modus ponens* and *modus tollens*. An example of a *modus ponens* inference is

(3)   If John is English then John is European
       John is English
∴ John is European

and an example of a *modus tollens* inference is

(4)   If John is English then John is European
       John is not European
∴ John is not English.

There has been disagreement among logicians about whether to say of inferences of this kind that the first two statements are premisses and the third the conclusion or that the first statement in each is a *rule of inference*, the second the premiss and the third the conclusion. However, that need not concern us here. What is important is that they are deductive infer-

ences since, like (1) and (2), their conclusions certainly
follow from their premises and their validity is a
formal matter.

The patterns of these inferences can be represented
by replacing their categorical statements by the
letters p and q, when we obtain

(3)a   If p then q
           p
$\therefore$ q

and

(4)a   If p then q
           Not q
$\therefore$ Not p.

We may read (3)a as "If p is true then q is true; p is
true; therefore q is true" and (4)a as "If p is true then
q is true; q is not true; therefore p is not true", where
p and q stand for any statements whatever. With a
little effort we can see, without reference to a particular subject matter, that these patterns of inference
are valid.

In each of our four examples, the validity depends,
as I have said, upon certain relations between the
component statements. These relations depend in
turn upon the meanings of certain words or symbols
in the statements and the arrangement of the symbolizing letters. For example, the validity of (1)a depends
upon "+" and "=", that of (2)a upon "all" and
"are", and that of (3)a and (4)a upon "if", "then"
and "not", together with the arrangement of the

symbolizing letters. The importance of this point can be brought out by considering

> All *B* is *A*
> All *C* is *A*
> ∴ All *C* is *B*

which is the same as (2)*a* except that the order of *A* and *B* in the first premiss has been reversed. This is an invalid inference pattern.

It is important, when we adopt this symbolizing procedure, to adhere to the convention that one letter stands always for the same subject-indicating term or statement. When we consider what is meant by "the same term or statement" our attention is drawn to a reservation which must be made in something I have already said. When we are considering actual inferences rather than inference patterns, we cannot always decide upon their validity in ignorance of their subject-matter; sometimes a knowledge of the subject-matter is necessary to enable us to decide whether what seems to be the same term appearing in two places is in fact the same term. Consider, as a crude and obvious example of this, the inference

> No physical object is red and green all over
> This striped ball is red and green all over
> ∴ This striped ball is not a physical object.

If we are incautious in replacing the subject-indicating terms by symbols we may obtain

> No *B* is *C*
> *x* is *C*
> ∴ *x* is not *B*,

which is a valid inference pattern. But the original inference is clearly invalid. This is because, although the same *words* "red and green all over" appear in the two premisses they are not used with the same meaning. In the first they mean "red all over and green all over" but in the second they do not. Therefore they cannot both be represented by *C*, and it is upon the appearance of *C* in both premisses that the validity of the inference pattern largely depends. Thus, although a knowledge of the subject-matter is unnecessary for seeing the validity of this inference pattern, and so of any inference which it *correctly* represents, it may be necessary to know something about the subject-matter of a given inference before we can see that it is of this pattern.

There are now two points to be made about the discussion so far. In the first place, when we use a symbol *p* to represent

John is English

or the expression

All *A* is *B*

to represent

All mammals are vertebrates

we are no longer dealing with statements; *p* and "All *A* is *B*" do not state anything. They merely represent forms of words which may be used to state something. Thus it does not make sense to talk of these representations as either true or false and this emphasizes the fact that in discussing the validity of various inference patterns we are not concerned with truth and falsity. Although the three lines of

      All A is B
      All C is A
$\therefore$ All C is B

cannot be used separately to state anything, they can, taken together, be regarded as asserting that it is allowable to move from two statements to a third, provided these statements have the forms indicated. That is, if this pattern can be regarded as stating anything at all, it cannot be regarded as stating something about the world but only as stating something about ways of talking about the world, that is, about the relations between certain kinds of statements.

In the second place, our patterns of inference may be regarded as being less distinct than they have so far been made to appear. We can bring this out, and further emphasize the irrelevance of actual truth and falsity to considerations of validity, by abstracting from our patterns of inference the relations upon which they depend. When we say "p, therefore q" we appear, misleadingly, to be talking as if p could be asserted. We can avoid this appearance by representing what we are really concerned about in this pattern of inference by the implication "If p then q" or "p implies q". Thus we can represent the implications underlying our patterns of inference (3)a and (4)a, respectively, by

(3)*b* If (If *p* then *q*,
     and *p*)
   then *q*

and

(4)*b* If (If *p* then *q*,
     and not *q*)
   then not *p*.

We can simplify these by writing "implies" in place of one appearance of "if ... then ...", obtaining

(3)*c* If *p* implies *q*,
     and *p*,
   then *q*

and

(4)*c* If *p* implies *q*,
     and not *q*,
   then not *p*.

The patterns of inference (1)*a* and (2)*a* are slightly more complex but we can now see that the underlying implications can be expressed in a similar way to those of (3)*a* and (4)*a*. Consider, again,

(1)*a* $a+b = c$ and (2)*a* All *A* is *B*
    $d+e = c$ All *C* is *A*
 $\therefore a+b = d+e$ $\therefore$ All *C* is *B*.

In each case we can represent the three expressions, respectively, by *p*, *q* and *r*. The inference pattern depends upon the fact that *p* and *q* together imply *r* and in making the inference we assert *p* and *q* and take this as entitling us to assert *r*. The implication upon which we depend is (*p* and *q*) implies *r*

and the basis of both inferences is

(1/2)*c*   If (*p* and *q*) implies *r*
and (*p* and *q*)
then *r*

Thus, although (1)*a* and (2)*a* look more complex than (3)*a*, the essential relations upon which they rest are the same, namely

(3)*c*   If *p* implies *q*,
and *p*,
then *q*

and their complexity lies only in the fact that *p* represents a compound categorical statement rather than a simple one. The syllogism, (2)*a*, may thus be regarded as a special case of the use of the rule of *modus ponens*, (3)*c*. If the expressions (1/2)*c*, (3)*c* and (4)*c* look oddly repetitious, it may be useful to think of them as explaining the implication relation, in the sense of showing how it may be used for particular inferences in particular contexts.

Finally, to return to our syllogism, (2)*a*, we express (2)*c*, its underlying pattern, more fully by replacing the original statement patterns for *p*, *q*, *r*, when we obtain

If (all *A* is *B* and all *C* is *A*) implies (all *C* is *B*)
and (all *A* is *B* and all *C* is *A*)
then (all *C* is *B*)

This is cumbersome and of no great practical use. What it does is to bring out that, when the statement patterns corresponding to *p*, *q* and *r* are as they are here, *p* and *q* *do in fact* imply *r*, and to show just why this is so. That is, the syllogism as it was originally represented, (2)*a*, exhibits one set of conditions in which *p* and *q* imply *r*.

Although the logician in his study of deductive inferences is concerned with only one aspect of these inferences, their validity, when we use deductive inferences in the course of our actual reasoning we do so in the hope that they will give us conclusions upon whose truth or acceptability we can rely. One thing that has emerged from this discussion is that an inference can lead us to conclusions about which we are justified in being certain if (1) we are certain that it is a deductively valid inference; and (2) we are certain that its premisses are true or acceptable without question. The field in which, *par excellence*, these conditions can be fulfilled is the field of pure mathematics. Such statements as "$2 + 2 = 4$" are the best, perhaps the only, examples of statements of whose "truth" or acceptability we can be certain. The pure mathematics we learn at school involves deductive inferences, and only deductive inferences.

6

DEDUCTIVE FALLACIES

So far we have considered only valid inferences, but it is important also to be able to recognize patterns which are not the patterns of valid inferences. There are many ways of committing fallacies in syllogistic arguments, which are given in detail in most text-books of traditional formal logic. Most of these fallacies, and, indeed, most of the fallacies of deductive inference generally, amount to very much the same thing. It may be said, informally, that they involve the assertion of conclusions which are wider than the evidence contained in the premisses permits.

This is perhaps best illustrated by the syllogistic fallacy of attempting to infer a universal conclusion from a particular premiss or from two particular premisses. One pattern which commits this fallacy is

All *B* is *C*
Some *A* is *B*
∴ All *A* is *C*.

Here, it is obvious that in asserting a universal conclusion we have gone beyond the evidence stated in the second premiss, for this asserted something of only *some A*'s and cannot constitute sufficient ground for an assertion about all *A*'s. Whenever an alleged conclusion asserts something about the whole of a class whereas the premisses make assertions only about part of that class, a fallacy is committed.

Another fallacious pattern is

Some B is C
All A is B
∴ All A is C

and this is less obviously fallacious because the term B does not appear in the conclusion, so that, at first sight, we do not seem to have gone beyond the evidence. The best way of describing what is wrong here is to say that since in both premisses reference is made to only some of the B's, the connection necessary for a deductive inference is not made. This is because we cannot be sure that the B's referred to in the first premiss are the same as those referred to in the second premiss; the B's which are A's may not be the B's which are C's

To take a specific example, consider

Some mammals are vegetarians
All cats are mammals
∴ All cats are vegetarians.

The second statement refers to all cats but only to some mammals, namely, the ones that are cats. In particular, it does not refer to those mammals which are mice, rabbits, and so on. The first statement may be referring to some other, quite different, section of the class of mammals; for all we are told, it may be only rabbits which are vegetarian mammals. Thus we have insufficient reason for concluding that all cats, or even some cats, have the property attributed to some section of the class of mammals by the first premiss. The term which is common to the two premisses of a syllogism is called the "middle" term and this fallacy is called "the fallacy of undistributed middle". To say that the middle term is undistributed is simply to say that it does not refer to the whole of the class of things it names. If it does not so refer, in at least one of the premisses, no deductive connection is established between the two premisses and no conclusion can be reached.

We may commit a fallacy of another sort by mistaking the properties of the relations involved in our statements. If, for example, we attempted to infer from

$$4 > 3$$
$$\text{and } 3 > 2$$
$$\text{to } 2 > 4$$

we should be assuming that "is greater than" is a symmetrical as well as a transitive relation. This, in fact, is so obvious a mistake that we are unlikely ever to make it, but comparable mistakes are possible. We are more likely, however, to commit fallacies by supposing that we have a transitive relation when we have not. For example,

a is next to b
b is next to c
$\therefore a$ is next to c.

As it stands, without further specification of the relation "is next to", this is a fallacy because we have a
non-transitive relation. That is, a, b and c may be
arranged like this:

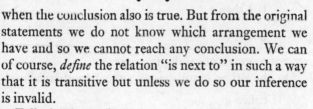

when the premisses are true and the conclusion false,
or like this:

when the conclusion also is true. But from the original
statements we do not know which arrangement we
have and so we cannot reach any conclusion. We can
of course, *define* the relation "is next to" in such a way
that it is transitive but unless we do so our inference
is invalid.

Fallacies in *modus-ponens* and *modus-tollens* inferences are perhaps of most importance for our present
purpose. The hypothetical statement

If p then q

tells us what follows if p is the case but not what
follows if p is not the case or what follows if q is the
case. For example, it does not follow from

If it is raining then the pavements are wet

that

If it is not raining then the pavements are not wet

since there are other possible causes of the pavements'
being wet, for example, a burst water main. For the
same reason, it does not follow from

If it is raining then the pavements are wet

that

If the pavements are wet then it is raining.

Thus, the two patterns

> If p then q
> Not p
> ∴ Not q

and

> If p then q
> q
> ∴ p

are not patterns of valid inferences.

On the other hand, because the hypothetical

> If p then q

tells us that q must be true if p is to be true, it follows that if q is not true, then p cannot be true, either. That is, inferences of the pattern

> If p then q
> Not q
> ∴ Not p

are valid.

Inferences may, of course, be based on statements of the form

> Not both p and q

and

> Either p or q,

and there are corresponding fallacies.

First, if we are given

> Not both p and q

we are told merely that p and q cannot both be true, so we can infer that if one is true, then the other cannot be. This does not imply that one of them must be true; we cannot infer that if one is not true then the other must be.

That is, the pattern

> Not both p and q
>   Not p
> ∴ q

is invalid.

A statement of the form

> Either p or q

tells us that one or the other is true but not both, if "either .... or ..." is used exclusively; it tells us that *at least one* is true if "either ... or ..." is used inclusively. Thus, on the exclusive use the following inference patterns are valid:

>   Either p or q (and not both)
>   Not p
> ∴ q

and

>   Either p or q (and not both)
> p
> ∴ Not q.

The only invalid patterns are so obviously invalid as to be unlikely to occur, namely:

> Either p or q (and not both)
> p
> ∴ q

and

> Either p or q (and not both)
> Not p
> ∴ Not q.

On the inclusive use, however, these two patterns are invalid but so is the pattern

> Either p or q
> p
> ∴ Not q.

Nothing excludes the possibility of both p and q being true, since "Either p or q" is to be read as "Either p or q (and possibly both)."

We may illustrate these points by the following example. If we are given

> Either John is clever or he is lucky (but not both)

we can infer thus:

> John is clever
> ∴ John is not lucky

or thus:

> John is not clever
> ∴ John is lucky.

But if we are given

Either John is clever or he is lucky (and possibly both)

it is invalid to infer thus:

John is clever
∴ John is not lucky

because the possibility of his being both is explicitly allowed. If "either . . . or . . ." is used without either bracketed expression it is taken in logic that the possibility of both alternatives being true is allowed; that is, it is taken in the inclusive sense.

7

PATTERNS OF REASONING: INDUCTION

The scientist is concerned to establish true state-ments about the world. He cannot, therefore, be interested merely in the validity of such deductive inferences as he uses, and must concern himself with the truth of their premisses and conclusions. In considering the way in which the scientist uses deductive inference we meet the other main kind of inference, *inductive* inference. We may approach this by considering the ways in which inferences may fail to justify our certainty about their conclusions.

(1) We may use a deductive inference without being certain of the truth of its premisses and the un-certainty of the premisses must infect our attitude to the conclusion. For example,

> All metals dissolve in nitric acid
> *a* is a metal
> ∴ *a* dissolves in nitric acid

is a valid deductive inference but it does not prove (the truth of) the conclusion. In fact, we know that the first premiss is false. But even if we did not know this we should not be justified in accepting the conclusion as absolutely certain as long as there was the remotest theoretical possibility of this premiss being false.

In the sciences there is always this theoretical possibility when we are dealing with general statements about natural phenomena. Although we know that this first premiss is false because gold, for instance, does not dissolve in nitric acid, we can conceive of a situation in chemistry in which attempts had been made to dissolve a great many different metals in nitric acid and all had succeeded. In this situation we might be inclined to suppose that the statement "All metals dissolve in nitric acid" was true. However, even in this situation, we could strictly do no more than entertain it as a hypothesis, and we should be unjustified in regarding it as certain. All the evidence we had would support it but all the evidence we had would not be all the evidence we could possibly get. For example, if we had tried to dissolve gold we should have obtained evidence against it. Moreover, even if we had found that all our samples of a particular metal, say silver, dissolved, this would leave open at least the theoretical possibility that some sample of silver as yet untested might, in the future, be found not to dissolve. Even if this result were highly improbable it would still not be impossible and this is enough to remove our justification for being absolutely certain of the conclusion of our deductive inference. The implication

> If all metals dissolve in nitric acid
> and *a* is a metal
> then *a* dissolves in nitric acid

would still hold, but as long as there is the slightest

possible doubt about the truth of the general statement, the inference based on it cannot give us
certainty, for *a* might happen to be the one metal
which does not dissolve.

All general statements about natural phenomena
have this provisional nature. What we have found to
be true of a number of examined samples of some
material never gives us the absolute right to assert
that the same will be true of all unexamined samples.
Thus we can never rely upon a deductive inference
which has such a general statement among its premisses to give us absolute certainty about its conclusion.
We are never logically justified in attaching to the
conclusion of a deductive inference more certainty
than we are justified in attaching to its premises.

This brings me to the second way in which inferences may fail to justify our certainty in their conclusions.

(2) If the scientist uses deductive inferences which
have general statements about phenomena, i.e.,
"empirical generalizations", as their premises he is,
implicitly or explicitly, relying on non-deductive
inferences for the support of those premises. The
implication relation involved in deductive inferences
may be called a "necessitating" relation; if one
statement implies another then the truth of the first
necessitates the truth of the second. This is the
strongest kind of relation between statements. But
the support for empirical generalizations depends upon
inferences involving weaker relations which may be

called, if the expression will be pardoned, "probabilifying" relations.

If we have evidence in support of, and no evidence
against, the statement

All metals dissolve in nitric acid

then the relation between that evidence and the
generalization is a probabilifying relation. In general,
the evidence in support of an empirical generalization
of the form

All *A* is *B*

is a statement of the form

All *examined A*'s are *B*.

In scientific contexts, all the examined A's are seldom,
if ever, all the *A*'s and so the statement of our
evidence is, speaking strictly, a particular statement
of the form

Some A is B.

Moving from a statement of this form to the universal
statement, as we do if we take our evidence as
sufficient to justify our acceptance of the universal
statement, is going beyond the evidence. This is not
to say that such a step is never justified but only to say
that it is not justified by the rules of deductive
inference. Although

All *A* is *B*

implies

Some *A* is *B*

except in certain special circumstances,

Some *A* is *B*

does not imply

All *A* is *B*.

It supports it, more or less strongly, but it never can support it up to the hilt. This sort of inference is usually called *inductive* inference and is often regarded as the pattern of inference typically used in the natural sciences.

Consider the inference

Some metals dissolve in nitric acid
x is a metal
∴ *x* dissolves in nitric acid.

In favourable circumstances we may be certain of the first two statements. But, even so, we cannot be certain of the conclusion, because we cannot be certain that *x* is one of the metals included in the term "some metals" of the first premiss. This prevents the relation between premisses and conclusion being a necessitating relation. Thus we cannot argue directly from the evidence for a generalization to a conclusion of which we are justified in being certain unless, of course, that conclusion formed part of the evidence and so is not new.

This is so even if we accept the more modest conclusion

x will probably dissolve in nitric acid

if we mean by this that

x is more likely than not to dissolve in nitric acid,

since we may, by accident, have examined just those metals which do dissolve and there may be an even larger number of unexamined metals which do not dissolve. Further, it is still an assumption that other, unexamined, samples of the same metal will behave in the same way as those already examined.

However, there is an inference about whose conclusion we could be justified in being certain, namely,

> Some metals dissolve in nitric acid
> x is a metal
> ∴ There is some probability that x dissolves in nitric acid

where the conclusion means that the evidence does not rule out the possibility of x's dissolving in nitric acid. Here, what we can be certain of is not any matter of fact about the possession of this property by x but only that the evidence we have still leaves open the possibility that x does possess this property.

Of course, there are ways of increasing the probability of our conclusions, in both the senses of probability indicated in the last two paragraphs, but since the amount of evidence we have is always less than the amount of evidence we could have, we can never convert this probability to certainty. In the sciences, the premisses for any deductive inferences we may use are frequently of this sort, so we are often not dealing with what might be called "pure" deductive inferences; we are also, even if only covertly, relying on inductive inference for the support of our premisses. In these cases we may support our conclusions more or less strongly but never *prove* them.

(3) The most extreme case is that in which we have neither a necessitating relation nor premisses of which we are justified in being certain. This situation often arises, especially in the early stages of a science. Consider, for example, the inference

> A barometric pressure of less than P has usually been followed by rain
>
> The barometric pressure, here and now, is less than P

∴ It will probably rain.

The relation between premisses and conclusion, here, is not a necessitating relation, because we cannot be certain that what has usually happened in the past will usually happen in the future. Moreover, we may very well be uncertain of our first premiss because of the incompleteness of meteorological records. Both these sources of uncertainty infect the conclusion.

It should be noted that we sometimes have a choice between two ways of expressing the kinds of scientific inference I have been discussing. This amounts to a choice of where to locate the source of uncertainty. We may express our inference in this way:

> All examined metals dissolve in nitric acid
>
> ∴ All metals dissolve in nitric acid
>
> x is a metal
>
> ∴ x will dissolve in nitric acid

where the first "∴" indicates an inductive step and

the second a deductive step and the uncertainty about
the conclusion is all generated by the first step. Or we
may express it thus:

> All examined metals dissolve in nitric acid
> ∴ Some metals dissolve in nitric acid
> x is a metal
> ∴ x will (probably) dissolve in nitric acid

where the first "∴" indicates a deductive step, since
it is a mere rewording, and the second an inductive
step, and the uncertainty of the conclusion is all generated by the second step. It does not matter greatly
which expression we adopt as long as we recognize
that at some point the justification for being certain
of the conclusion, in the way in which we can be
certain of a deductive conclusion from unquestionable
premisses, is eliminated.

These formulations also show that it is misleading
to say, as has often been said, that induction is "inference from the particular to the general". It may be
but it need not be. We may more effectively cover the
cases in which the so-called "problem of induction"
is raised by regarding it as inference which, by the
canons of deductive inference, goes beyond the
evidence.

Another way of exhibiting the place of inductive
inference in the sciences is by considering the logic of
the procedure by which we test, and come to accept,
hypotheses. Suppose we entertain a hypothesis, which
I represent by p, from which we deduce certain

observable consequences, which I represent by q, r and s. That is to say, we find that if p is true then q, r and s, being implied by it, must be true also. Since q, r and s are *observable* consequences we can set up the conditions under which, if p is true, they should occur, and see if they do occur. If they do, we regard this as supporting the hypothesis. Putting this in another way, q, r and s are predictions based on p and whose fulfilment counts in favour of p.

Now the pattern of this inference is

> If p then q, r and s
> q, r and s
> ∴ p

and this, according to the canons of deductive inference, is invalid. It is like arguing

> If John is English then John is European
> John is European
> ∴ John is English

and in a similar way "goes beyond the evidence". It is, therefore, an inductive inference. Further, although it would be invalid if it were claimed as a deductive inference, it is an inductive inference which we frequently accept and regard as justified.

The problem of induction has figured largely in discussion among philosophers of science and it is raised by the sort of situation I have been considering. It is unreasonable to say that we are not justified in relying upon inductive conclusions; we constantly do so, it would be difficult to get on without doing so, and our reliance upon them has borne much fruit. What has worried logicians is the difficulty of finding a logical basis for our belief that we are justified in relying on them. It is possible to point to logical principles which constitute a general justification for deductive inferences of various kinds, but it does not seem to be possible to do the same for inductive inferences.

Clearly, since inductive conclusions can never be held with the same kind of certainty as deductive conclusions in, say, pure mathematics, and cannot be regarded as never requiring revision, we cannot expect the justification of induction to be of the same kind as the justification of deduction. The question is, can we expect to find any kind of *general* justification for induction?

There is another way in which the problems of justification in these two fields are not comparable. What the rules of deductive inference justify our being certain about is not strictly the truth of deduced conclusions but merely that the conclusions follow from the premisses. When we are justified in being certain of the truth of these conclusions, we can never be justified solely on the grounds that the rules of deductive inference have been obeyed. This only assures us that *if* the premisses are true then so are the conclusions. In pure mathematics, about which it is often said that deductive inferences give us conclusions which are final and indubitable, this is because, apart from the mere validity of the inferences, we are assured of the unquestioned acceptability of our premisses. The problem of induction can then be regarded as involving a comparison between our premisses in pure mathematics and in natural science, a question about how it is that we are more strongly assured of the former than the latter and a question about our justification for relying upon premisses of whose truth we are not completely assured.

The problem of induction has, in fact, been complicated by a misconception which resulted from missing this point. It is a mistake to compare the justification of induction with the justification of deduction. The justification of deduction depends on showing how conclusions follow from premisses: a justification of induction could not take this form because, by definition, the conclusions do not *follow* from the premisses. What it must involve is the elucidation of the relations between statements of conclusions and the evidence for them.

Attempts to solve the problem of induction have ranged from clearly misguided attempts to show that induction is really deduction to the modest assertion that we must just go on using it because it works. It has lately been denied that the problem of induction is an important one for the philosophy of science. Among the grounds upon which this has been denied are that induction is not a method which is used in the sciences, that to ask for a general justification of induction is senseless because it is to ask an unanswerable question, and that to ask this is to misunderstand the meanings of certain words, such as "justification", "reason", "certainty" and "doubt".

In this connection, it is illuminating to note that there is a great difference between asking for a justification of inductive inference in general and asking for a justification for particular inductive conclusions. To ask for a general justification is at least to suggest that it might be possible to give a formal justification for induction which is independent of the subject matter of any particular induction. To ask for a justification for a particular inductive conclusion, on the other hand, is simply to ask about the weight of the evidence for that particular conclusion. The difficulty of conceiving what kind of formal justification could be given has led some philosophers to suggest that the second question is the only legitimate one.

Finally, it is important to note that induction may be thought of in two ways which have not always been distinguished. When we say that scientists use induction we may mean that they reach some of their conclusions by inferring inductively from their evidence, conceiving induction as a *procedure* by which discoveries are made or conclusions reached; or we may mean that, however they reach their conclusions, they support them by induction, conceiving induction as a relation between evidence and conclusions upon which scientists rely. If we confuse these two conceptions we are likely to get into serious difficulties in trying to decide whether scientists use induction or not.

8

POSSIBILITY AND NECESSITY

I have used the phrases "logical necessity" and "logically necessary" and these, together with the associated terms "logically possible" and "logically impossible", require some elucidation. I shall begin with possibility.

First, it is important to distinguish between *logical* and *practical* possibility and impossibility. It is logically impossible to see an invisible man, even if there were such a thing, because if we could see him he would not be invisible. It is logically impossible for there to be a married bachelor, because a bachelor is *defined* as unmarried. It is logically impossible for there to be states of affairs describable in those ways for the alleged descriptions are self-contradictory. That is, the statements

I see an invisible man

and

John is a married bachelor

are self-contradictory. If we are familiar with the meanings of the words used in these statements we can see that they are self-contradictory merely by examining the statements themselves; there is no need to examine John or men, visible or invisible, to discover this.

These self-contradictory statements are related to statements which are often called *analytic* or *tautologous*. For example, the two statements

> Invisible men cannot be seen

and

> Bachelors are unmarried

are analytic because they merely draw out the meaning, or part of the meaning, of "invisible" and "bachelors", respectively. They are part of an analysis of these terms. It is a consequence of the meaning of "invisible" that the first statement is, and must necessarily be, true, for it just states part of this meaning; it is a consequence of the meaning of "bachelor" that the second statement is and must be true, for the same reason. These are *logical necessities*. That is, it is logically necessary, given certain facts about the English language, that they be true and logically impossible that they be false.

The two statements

> No-one can see an invisible man

and,

> I can see an invisible man

contradict one another; the first is necessarily true and the second is self-contradictory. The second is the negation of the first, so it can be said that self-contradictory statements, those whose truth is *logically* impossible, are the negations of analytic statements, those whose truth is logically necessary.

It is logically possible for men to fly to Venus even if, at the moment, it is practically impossible; it is both logically and practically possible to send a rocket to the moon. The statement

A man has landed on Venus

is not self-contradictory, so its truth is logically possible; its negation is not self-contradictory, so its truth is not logically necessary.

What is logically possible may or may not be practically possible; what is logically impossible is clearly practically impossible as well. Mere practical impossibilities may be overcome by technical developments but logical impossibilities cannot; we may develop rockets capable of landing men on Venus but we could not possibly develop instruments for seeing invisible men. If we did they would no longer be invisible. A man may be invisible, to a particular observer at a particular time with the naked eye; if we provide this observer with a telescope this does not enable him to see an invisible man but only a man who *was* invisible and is now, just because he is seen, visible. The telescope turns an invisible man into a visible man.

We may say that something that is logically impossible is something that is not allowed by the laws of logic and language, whereas something that is practically impossible is something that is not allowed by the techniques at present available. A further distinction is sometimes made between practical and *physical* possibilities and impossibilities. A physical impossibility is something which conflicts with laws of nature, but not with laws of logic. For instance, it may be logically possible to land a rocket on the sun but not physically possible, because no material of which the rocket could be made would withstand the great heat. If this is so, then this would be practically impossible as well, for no technical advance can nullify what is a law of nature. On the other hand, if it were possible to develop a material which would withstand the heat on the surface of the sun this would mean that, as far as this condition was concerned, it was physically possible to land a rocket on the sun because we should have shown that it is not, after all, a law of nature that no material will withstand this heat. It still might not be practically possible to perform this feat. What is physically impossible is also practically impossible, but what is physically possible may not be practically possible.

Logical possibilities are related to statements which are often called *synthetic*. While it is logically impossible for bachelors to be married men, it is logically possible for the statement

    All bachelors are bald

to be true, although it happens to be false. This is a *synthetic* statement, to be contrasted with analytic statements, because it does not merely elucidate the meaning of some of its terms but *adds* something about bachelors which is not contained in the meaning of "bachelors". Although it is contradicted by

Some bachelors are not bald,

this statement, the negation of the original statement, is not self-contradictory; indeed, it happens to be true. Neither is the statement

No bachelors are bald

self-contradictory, although it happens to be false. These three statements are all synthetic and their truth is both logically and practically possible. All synthetic statements state logical possibilities but not necessarily physical or practical possibilities. For example,

Men can fly without apparatus

states a logical possibility but a physical and practical impossibility.

Analytic statements are sometimes said to be *logically true* and self-contradictory statements *logically false* while synthetic statements are said to be *factually true* or *false*, as the case may be. The distinction between analytic and synthetic statements is based upon the characteristics of the statements themselves. That is, whether a statement is analytic or synthetic depends upon whether its truth depends merely upon the meaning of some terms in it or not;

or upon whether its negation is self-contradictory or not.

Logicians frequently make another distinction between kinds of statements which must not be confused with the analytic-synthetic distinction. That is the distinction between *a priori* and *a posteriori* (or *empirical*) statements. It is based not upon the forms of the statements themselves, but upon the ways in which they can be supported or known to be true. To say that a statement is *a priori* is to say that it can be known to be true independently of, or in advance of, experience of its subject-matter; that we do not require *evidence* in support of it. To say that a statement is *a posteriori* is to say that it can only be known to be true through experience of its subject-matter; that we do require evidence in support of it.

The statement

A bald man is a man

is *a priori*, since it can be seen to be true by anyone who is familiar with the English language, whether he has ever seen any bald men or not. Its truth depends upon the meanings of certain English words rather than upon the characteristics of any particular bald men. On the other hand, a knowledge of the English language alone will not enable us to decide whether the statement

Bald men tend to be bad-tempered

is true or not. To decide this we should have to examine bald men and their behaviour.

A priori statements may thus be established once and for all, given only that the meanings of the words in them do not change, whereas *a posteriori* statements are open to revision in the light of future experience. If we examined 1,000 bald men and found that 900 of them were bad-tempered, we should be to some extent justified in concluding that bald men tend to be bad-tempered. But an examination of a further 2,000 bald men might reveal that 1,900 of these were not bad-tempered. That is, out of 3,000 bald men we should now have found only 1,000 bad-tempered ones. We should thus have to revise our original conclusions and on further investigation we might have to revise our conclusion once again. But no future experience can alter our belief that a bald man is a man.

An important controversy in logic and philosophy concerns the relation between the analytic-synthetic classification, on the one hand, and the *a priori–a posteriori* classification, on the other. At first sight it looks as if these must always demarcate the same groups of statements, as if analytic statements must always be *a priori* and synthetic statements must always be *a posteriori*. This, however, has been denied on grounds that are by no means negligible, and it has been argued that there are also statements which are both synthetic and *a priori*. It has, for example, been held by many philosophers that mathematical statements, from the simplest to the most complex, are analytic and *a priori* but it has been held by another powerful body of philosophers that they are synthetic and *a priori*. This is of interest to philosophers of science because it raises the question whether some statements in the sciences, which at first would seem to be synthetic and *a posteriori*, are in fact synthetic and *a priori*. No-one, as far as I know, has argued that there are analytic *a posteriori* statements, for reasons which should by now be obvious.

I have explained logical, physical and practical possibility and logical necessity, but I have not discussed *physical* and *practical necessity*. Practical necessity is not of great importance and can quickly be got out of the way. We might say that it is necessary for a man to have £500 a year before he gets married. This is neither a logical necessity nor a physical necessity for neither logical, linguistic nor physical laws prevent a man's marrying on less; it is a mere practical necessity, since what would prevent his marrying would be the thought of the discomforts and inconveniences which would follow.

Necessities are sometimes indicated in ordinary speech by the use of the word "must". If we say, "A bachelor must be unmarried", we indicate a logical necessity and if we say, "A man must have £500 a year before he marries", we indicate a practical necessity. But there is another, and more controversial, use of "must" which lies somewhere between these two. We sometimes say such things as, "In view of the known laws and established theories about the structure and behaviour of gases, any sample of gas which is heated while its pressure is kept constant *must* expand." This "must" is said by some philosophers to indicate a physical or natural necessity, by others to indicate a mistaken view of the world on the part of anyone making the statement.

The central question here is whether the natural world is such that we can say that given certain conditions, certain events *must* occur, that is, will necessarily occur. Do some scientific laws state physical or natural necessities? There is a strong empiricist tradition, especially in British and American philosophy, within which this question is usually answered with a firm "No!" According to this view, what scientific laws do state is relations which as a matter of fact usually hold but which need not. This is a complex problem about which, here, I can do no more than give notice.

I have discussed logical necessity in connection with analytic statements, but it is important also in connection with valid deductive inferences. The conclusions of valid deductive inferences follow with logical necessity, which fact is sometimes indicated by "must" in their conclusions, thus:

> All mammals are vertebrates
> All gorillas are mammals
> ∴ All gorillas must be vertebrates.

This "must" may be taken as indicating also that the inference, taken as a whole, is analytic and that the conclusion follows with logical necessity just because what is stated in the conclusion is already implicit in or "contained in" the premisses. All deductive inference may be regarded as analytic in this sense, and this may be regarded as accounting for the certainty it gives.

Finally, I may sum up the main points about possibility and necessity which I have made in this section in the following way:

Practical possibility *implies* physical possibility *implies* logical possibility.

Logical impossibility *implies* physical impossibility *implies* practical impossibility.

Logical necessity *implies* physical necessity *implies* practical necessity.

These implications do not hold the other way round.

It may further be noted that if a definition of a particular word states that it means the same as, or is equivalent to, another word or group of words, then the statement of the definition is an analytic statement. For example, the statement, in classical mechanics, that momentum is the product of mass and velocity, is an analytic statement.

9

DEFINITION

Definitions establish logical necessities and logical impossibilities. If swans are defined as, among other things, white, then it is logically impossible, while we accept this definition, to find a swan of any other colour and logically necessary that any swan we find be white. This might be expressed differently. We might say that a definition proposes a rule of language which, in accepting it, we decide to obey. Then our definition of swans as white determines what we shall say when, in the future, we are confronted by white and non-white birds having swan-like characteristics. But this is another subject which is fraught with controversy and even to put it like this is to take sides.

Traditionally, that which is to be defined is the *definiendum* and that which defines it is the *definiens*. The point of defining may be put in logical or psychological terms. Logically, in defining we state how a symbol or set of symbols may be replaced in an expression without altering the meaning or the truth of that expression, or what a symbol or set of symbols means in terms of symbols whose meaning is already established. The psychological aspect of this is that we facilitate the understanding of a symbol or set of symbols by showing their relations to symbols which are already understood. We may proceed in two ways. We may relate existing, accepted symbols to one another, or we may establish an equivalence between a set of existing, accepted symbols and a new symbol. In either case, what is taken as already understood is the *definiens*; because it is taken as understood it is suitable for defining something which is, up to this point, not understood, or not clearly understood. From the logical point of view, the *definiens* and the *definiendum* may, once the definition is accepted, replace one another in contexts in which the definition is meant to apply. In mathematics and logic, definitions are often regarded as mere abbreviations adopted for the sake of brevity and comprehensibility.

I have been speaking of "symbols" because, of course, we define other sorts of symbol besides words—for example, in mathematics and cartography. This should be borne in mind whenever I speak of defining "words", "phrases" or "expressions".

Perhaps the most fundamental disagreement in this field has concerned the question whether definitions are *real* or *nominal* (verbal). A *nominal* definition asserts a determination to use a certain expression as an exact equivalent and substitute for another expression. In this kind of definition the meaning of the *definiendum* depends solely upon that of the *definiens*; the definition gives the entire meaning of the expression defined. It follows from the fact that a nominal definition asserts simply a particular intention, that it is itself neither true nor false. It is a convention and, to some extent, arbitrary.

A *real* definition states that two expressions, each of which has an independent meaning, are equivalent to one another. Suppose, for example, that we know what "good" means, at least in the sense that we use the word successfully in communicating with one another. Now, if "good" is defined as "conducive to the greatest happiness of the greatest number", this is a real definition if the meaning of this expression is originally independent of the meaning of "good". We know the meanings of both expressions prior to definition; in defining we equate the two. Such a definition is either true or false since it either is or is not the case that, to continue our example, "good" and "conducive to the greatest happiness of the greatest number" are already used as equivalent in meaning.

It is sometimes said, for obvious reasons, that the *definiens* of a real definition provides an *analysis* of the *definiendum*. The contrast between nominal and real definitions might be put, epigrammatically, by saying that nominal definitions are decided upon, real definitions are discovered.

It has also been regarded as a matter of controversy whether we define words or things or, more accurately, expressions or what the expressions apply to. This question has come in for much discussion, in spite of the fact that there are reasons for thinking that it rests entirely upon a misconception; here we must be content to notice that it does not make sense to ask what a table means but it does make sense to ask what the word "table" means. Moreover, in saying what the word "table" means we are saying something about everything to which the word applies, that is, about tables. Words and things are so closely related that it is almost impossible, in the context we are considering, to say something about words without saying something about things. The question whether we define words or things admits only of the answer that we define words but this is not to exclude our saying, at the same time and in the very act, something about things.

A definition may be arbitrary but it need not be. If I wish to speak often about some complex which has not been regularly spoken about before I may, for the sake of brevity, arbitrarily choose or invent a word to stand for the complex. Suppose, for example, that I wish to refer frequently to logicians of Polish origin who are naturalized Americans. I might, to avoid the use of this cumbersome expression, decide to call them by the invented word "Pologams". The arbitrariness lies in my using just that word, rather than others, to serve my particular purpose. Such a situation is rare and we more usually wish to define an existing expression in terms of other existing expressions whose meanings are known; then the defining activity is largely controlled by the ways in which those expressions are already used, and so is not arbitrary.

It has sometimes been thought that an expression could be defined by enumerating typical examples of things to which the expression is used to refer. We might, for instance, define "gorilla" by mentioning the inhabitants of particular cages in the London zoo, the Berlin zoo and the New York zoo. Then, it is said, anyone who is familiar with these inhabitants would be able to gather what "gorilla" means. Such definition has been called *extensive* definition but it is doubtful if it deserves to be called "definition" at all. The main difficulty is that, unless we mention the characteristics in view of which we call these specimens "gorillas", it will be difficult for the person learning the word to know just when to apply it in, say, the Moscow zoo and the Tokyo zoo.

Closely related to this alleged kind of definition, and suffering from a similar lack of precision, is the so-called *ostensive* definition, to which considerable importance has been, misguidedly, attached in recent years. Consider the question, "Is it possible, logically possible, to define every word in the English language in terms of other words in the English language?" Clearly the answer must be "No". Unless we can take for granted the meanings of some words we shall either move endlessly in circles or we shall define some words in terms of others whose meanings are not known. The way out of the circle and the method of providing a starting-point, it has been argued, is through ostensive definition. (There are other reasons for which it has been thought to be important.) We define ostensively when we utter a word while pointing to the things to which it applies. For example, I might teach a child what "red" means by pointing to various objects having the appropriate colour, saying "red" each time I did so. It has been held that a number of our simplest and most basic words are historically, and must logically be, learnt in this way.

Whatever the truth of this, it is misleading to regard this process as definition, just as it is misleading to regard extensive definition as definition and, further, a serious confusion may be involved in the whole way of talking which I have just been considering. However important definition may be, we must not suppose that we always and only learn our language through definitions, or the association of some narrow and precise meaning with each word or expression. Defining is a fairly sophisticated process which depends upon having learnt a good deal of the language in question and upon having discovered how a language, in general, works. Moreover, the usefulness of definition varies according to context. We may, for example, define "force" shortly in a way which is perfectly adequate for, say, classical mechanics but which is hardly adequate for an understanding of the many everyday uses of the word. The only way of coming to an understanding of the word as it is commonly used is through the hearing and using of it in the various appropriate contexts. Most of our words and expressions involve far more subtleties than can be captured in short and economical definitions. Definitions are of most use in specific restricted contexts, such as those of the various sciences, where it is desirable to "fossilize" a term and limit the richness of its meaning. The difference between everyday and scientific discourse is not merely that in everyday discourse we have not reached the ideal of having defined all our terms whereas in scientific discourse we have, but rather that everyday discourse is such that this is not an ideal for it.

10

NECESSARY AND SUFFICIENT CONDITIONS

Logicians and philosophers of science, as well as mathematicians, are inclined to talk of the necessary and sufficient conditions of something's being the case.

A *necessary condition* of something is a condition without whose fulfilment that something cannot occur or be the case.

A *sufficient condition* of something is a condition whose fulfilment ensures that that something occurs or is the case.

A *necessary and sufficient condition* of something is a condition whose fulfilment ensures that that something occurs or is the case and without whose fulfilment that something would not occur or be the case.

This is most easily understood in connection with the truth of statements. If p and q are statements then p is a sufficient condition of q if the truth of p ensures the truth of q and a necessary condition if q cannot be true unless p is true. This may be most clearly illustrated, first, by a mathematical example. Consider the equation

$$x+y = 5.$$

If x and y are positive whole numbers it is a necessary condition of this equation's holding that either x or y, but not both, be an odd number, since the sum of two odd numbers and the sum of two even numbers are always even. It is a sufficient condition that $x = 2$ and $y = 3$ but this is not a necessary condition, since other sufficient conditions are that $x = 3$ and $y = 2$ and that $x = 4$ and $y = 1$. However, given that $x = 2$, then it is the necessary and sufficient condition that $y = 3$. On the other hand, given that $x = 3$, then it is the necessary and sufficient condition that $y = 2$. There are, in fact, four sufficient conditions for the truth of $x+y = 5$, as we have ruled out 0 as a value for x and y, namely

(1) $x = 1, y = 4$;
(2) $x = 2, y = 3$;
(3) $x = 3, y = 2$;
(4) $x = 4, y = 1$.

Each of these fulfils the necessary condition that one value be odd and the other even and also the other necessary condition that each value be less than 5. If we are given a particular value for x, then the corresponding value for y becomes a necessary and also the sufficient condition for the truth of the equation.

In general, if p is a sufficient condition of q then p implies q, for example, $(x = 1, y = 4)$ implies $(x+y = 5)$; if p is a necessary condition of q then q implies p, for example, $(x+y = 5)$ implies (x or y is odd); if p is a necessary and sufficient condition of q then both p implies q and q implies p, for example, $(x+y = 5$, if $x = 1)$ implies and is implied by $y = 4$. It follows also that if p is a necessary condition of q then q is a sufficient condition of p for both are true if q implies p.

If we are given merely the equation $x+y = 5$ the necessary conditions of its truth are so general that they do not give us much help in deciding on the actual values to be assigned to x and y. If we are given another equation, and told that it is simultaneously true, for example, $x-y = 3$, we can arrive at the necessary and sufficient conditions for the truth of the two equations together. In "solving" simultaneous equations our aim is to find necessary and sufficient conditions for their truth, although we sometimes have to be content with sufficient conditions. In our example, we can arrive at necessary and sufficient conditions, thus:

$$x+y = 5$$
$$x-y = 3$$
$$\overline{}$$
$$2x = 8$$
$$\therefore x = 4$$
$$\therefore y = 1$$

If, however, we consider the equations $x^2+y^2 = 40$ and $x^2-y^2 = 32$, and negative integers are not ruled out, we can solve them, thus,

$$x^2+y^2 = 40$$
$$x^2-y^2 = 32$$

$$2x^2 = 72$$
$$x^2 = 36$$
$$\therefore x = \pm 6$$
$$\therefore y = \pm 2$$

Here we can arrive at four sets of sufficient conditions, namely, $x = 6$, $y = 2$; $x = -6$, $y = -2$; $x = 6$, $y = -2$; $x = -6$, $y = 2$. Further equations would be needed to enable us to arrive at necessary and sufficient conditions.

Similar things can be said about physical situations, although here there are more complexities. For example, conditions which are jointly sufficient for the explosion of petrol vapour are:

(1) That a certain proportion of oxygen be mixed with it.
(2) That certain other substances be not mixed with it.
(3) That its temperature be raised to a certain point.

These are also necessary conditions if there is no other substance besides oxygen that will do and if an explosion could not be produced by, for example, mixing with it another substance which would act as a catalyst and so eliminating the necessity for raising its temperature. However, assuming these things, if (1) and (2) are satisfied then (3) is a necessary and also a sufficient condition of the occurrence of an explosion. It is a sufficient condition that the temperature be raised with a lighted match, but not a necessary condition, because it is also a sufficient condition that it be done with an electrically heated wire.

It is sometimes thought desirable to give an account of *causation* in terms of necessary and sufficient conditions. This has the appearance of imparting a certain logical rigour to discussions of this topic, but care is needed when we move from talk about the necessary and sufficient conditions for the truth of statements to the necessary and sufficient conditions for the occurrence of events. If, for example, we say that the cause of an event is the necessary and sufficient conditions for the occurrence of that event, we must note that the concept of cause involves the notion of temporal order whereas the concept of necessary and sufficient conditions need not, and, as we have used it so far, does not. It seems, therefore, advisable to distinguish between the necessary and sufficient conditions for the truth of a statement and the necessary and sufficient conditions for the occurrence of an event.

It is a necessary condition of the truth of

   a is a cat

that it be true that

   a is a mammal;

and it is a sufficient condition of the truth of

   a is a mammal

that it be true that

   a is a cat.

But there is no sense in asking whether *a* was a mammal first and a cat later, or vice versa.

Now consider two statements concerned with the occurrence of events. If pure petrol vapour is mixed in a certain proportion with pure oxygen, a sufficient condition of the truth of

> The mixture exploded

is the truth of

> A lighted match was applied to the mixture.

Therefore, a necessary condition of the truth of

> A lighted match was applied to the mixture

is the truth of

> The mixture exploded.

At first sight, this may look odd, because it looks as if we are saying that *before* a lighted match could be applied to the mixture it must have exploded. But this is clearly not so. Because we are talking of the relations between the truth or falsity of these statements we can say that a necessary condition of the truth of

> A lighted match was applied to the mixture at time t_1

is the truth of

> The mixture exploded at time t_2

where t_1 is *earlier* than t_2. The language of necessary and sufficient conditions, as used here, is intended to convey that the first statement cannot be true *unless* the second statement is true and not that the second must be true earlier in time than the first. It is not intended to convey something about the *order* of occurrence of the events to which the statements refer.

However, we may say that the application of heat to the mixture is a sufficient condition of the occurrence of an explosion, meaning to indicate that the first event will later be followed by the second. But then, is it possible to say that the occurrence of the explosion is a necessary condition of the application of heat to the mixture, since this appears to reverse the time-order? This is certainly to use "necessary condition" in a different sense from that in which we use it when we say that it is a necessary condition of the explosion of the mixture that the mixture contain petrol vapour and oxygen in a certain proportion, meaning that you must get the mixture right *first* if you want to produce an explosion.

If we talk of events as necessary and/or sufficient conditions of other events, then it seems that we cannot say that if the occurrence of e_1 is a sufficient condition of the occurrence of e_2, then the occurrence of e_2 is a necessary condition of the occurrence of e_1. We can only say that this relation holds between p and q where these are statements about the occurrence of these events. Thus it is a matter for discussion whether the statement that e_1 causes e_2, a relation between events, can be analyzed into statements about certain physical conditions being necessary and/or sufficient for the occurrence of certain events.

11

GENERALIZATIONS, HYPOTHESES AND LAWS

Early "inductivist" accounts of the sciences, allegedly stemming largely from the work of Francis Bacon, tended to regard scientific conclusions as generalizations from particular instances. According to this view, science begins with the observing of similarities and differences between different substances or different things or different events which allow the making of generalizations from these particular instances. The one basic method of all the sciences is generalization and the advance of science consists in the making of wider and wider generalizations, first from particular instances and later from generalizations, to higher and wider generalizations. That is, the advance of science consists in a series of inductive inferences.

A *hypothesis* was regarded as a generalization which is entertained but not yet sufficiently supported by evidence to be accepted with confidence; a *law* was regarded as a generalization for which sufficient evidence has been obtained to warrant its being taken as established, at least for the time being; a *theory* was sometimes regarded as a higher generalization about laws. For example, the account of the development of scientific knowledge of the behaviour of gases went something like this. On the basis of the observation of the behaviour of gases under certain conditions, certain hypotheses were entertained about the relations between the pressure, volume and temperature of gases. These were in the form of generalizations about these relations for all gases, embodying the assumption that unexamined gases would behave, in the given conditions, in similar ways to the examined gases. When sufficient numbers of instances of the behaviour of the available gases under these conditions had been observed, the hypotheses became laws, and we have, for example, Boyle's Law and Charles's Law. Further generalizations *from these laws* led to the formulation of a theory about the structure of all gases, the Kinetic Theory, according to which gases are even more alike, in certain ways, than they are stated to be by the elementary laws.

This way of putting it, although it had some justification, has gradually been modified and the idea that all scientific conclusions are generalizations from particular instances of events or laws has received severe criticism. It is especially implausible to represent scientific theories as generalizations from laws. What has partly been responsible for misleading philosophers of science is, perhaps, the undeniable fact that hypotheses, laws and theories are, alike, general.

It is important to see that what I am drawing attention to here is changes in the accounts of

scientific method rather than changes in the methods
themselves. It is not that formerly scientists used a
method advocated by Bacon and have in recent years
abandoned it, but rather that commentators on the
sciences formerly tended to accept the "Baconian"
description of scientific method but now tend to be
critical of it.

It is useful to distinguish between a *general
statement* and a *generalization*. Calling a statement a
"generalization" suggests that it was in fact arrived at
by generalizing, by arguing from particular instances
to a statement about all instances of the same thing,
whereas calling it "general" does not suggest anything
about the way in which it was reached. A general
statement may be arrived at in many different ways,
including guessing; generalizing is only one of the
ways of arriving at a general statement.

If I say

All okapis have two stomachs

I am making a general statement about okapis which
may or may not be true. I do not know which because
I know very little about okapis and have certainly
never examined any so I cannot be said to have arrived
at it by generalizing. I, therefore, would not say that
this is a generalization of mine. If it happens to be true
then I have made a true general statement about okapis
but I have still not made a generalization. I may,
having made the statement without knowing whether
it is true or not, then set about gathering evidence for

and against it and eventually show that it is true. Then I should have supported a general statement without ever generalizing. Calling a statement "general" is saying something about the range of its applicability, whereas calling it a "generalization" it *also* saying something about how it was reached.

Few, if any, philosophers would deny that all scientific laws are general but many would deny that they are all generalizations, in this sense. In fact, there are very good reasons for saying that some scientific conclusions are generalizations and equally good reasons for saying that others are not, even if all are general. The more elementary general statements of the various branches of science, statements which are merely classificatory, tend to be generalizations; among these, for example, are the statements we meet early in the study of inorganic chemistry which assert that particular substances have particular properties such as solubility in water.

On the other hand, certain scientific conclusions clearly are not, and could not be, merely generalizations from particular instances. The gas laws are accepted as general statements about "ideal" or "perfect" gases and, therefore, could not be generalizations since ideal or perfect gases are so defined that instances of them could not be observed. They are idealizations to which the behaviour of all actual, observable gases approximates. Even more clearly, general statements, in the classical Kinetic Theory, about the particles of which gases are said to be composed could not be generalizations from particular instances of the behaviour of those particles. Hypotheses and laws about things of which there could not be observed instances are conveniently called *non-instantial* hypotheses and laws. A *non-instantial* law could not be a generalization; an *instantial* law may be but it need not be. Newton's laws of motion and the conclusions of modern physics about fundamental particles are similarly, but not necessarily always for the same reasons, non-instantial.

When we examine the more advanced regions of the sciences it becomes obvious that the scientist is usually engaged in doing things which are very different from patient observation and careful generalization. What he does is more nearly described by saying that, knowing a large number of facts about the behaviour of what he is studying, he casts about for plausible hypotheses which will connect and explain these facts. He does not, like the mathematician, argue in a rigorous and controlled way from his data to a conclusion which is the only one possible. His casting about may involve guesswork, trial and error or the noticing of analogies with otherwise unrelated fields and his conclusion may be only the most plausible of a number of possible alternatives. This is not a criticism of scientific methods; the material with which the scientist works determines that procedures of this kind are often the only ones available to the scientist which are both rational and profitable.

There are different sorts of hypotheses and it is one of the tasks of the philosophy of science to distinguish these and to show how they are established and how they function in scientific investigation. There are, for example, hypotheses which merely attribute properties to substances and hypotheses which attribute ideal properties to ideal entities. There are both qualitative and quantitative hypotheses. Some hypotheses state numerical constants, for instance, boiling-points and melting-points; others state functional relations between these, for instance, the variation of boiling-point with pressure. There are hypotheses which help to explain phenomena by pointing to causes or postulating unobserved events upon which observed events depend.

One prerequisite of a good hypothesis, of whatever kind, is that it should be capable of *deductive development*, that is, it should be possible to deduce from it, along with other, accepted, statements, consequences which are capable of being tested, in one way or another, by making observations and experiments. Even the simplest generalization may be capable of deductive development of the requisite sort, for it is an accepted deductive principle, as well as a common-sense truth, that a general statement applies to each one of its instances. Thus it is a rudimentary deduction from "All gases expand on heating" that "This gas expands on heating", even if it is so rudimentary that we should not often regard it as necessary to point out that it is a deduction. More complex

hypotheses are likely to yield more deductions covering different but related phenomena. Here, the
connections between hypotheses and statements
which can be directly checked against observations
are likely to be through considerably longer chains of
deduction.

What can be deduced from a hypothesis, together
with other, accepted, statements may be regarded as
predictions made from this hypothesis. Thus, it may
be said that the testing of a hypothesis involves the
making of observations or experiments to discover
whether these predictions are fulfilled or not. A
hypothesis may be accepted and become a law when a
sufficient number of these predictions has been fulfilled, or, as some philosophers would wish to say,
when our most strenuous efforts to show that these
predictions are unfulfilled have failed. Whichever way
we put it, there remains an important and difficult
question concerning the meaning of "sufficient
number" and "most strenuous efforts".

I have said something already (p. 73) about the
logic involved in the testing of hypotheses through the
predictions which can be made from them. All I wish
to add here about this is that even if we believe that
generalization is utterly unimportant as a procedure in
the sciences, still we must admit that the inductive
relation enters into the supporting of hypotheses, at
least in the sense that the supporting evidence we have
for a general statement is always less than the evidence
we might have.

It has been held that prediction is the central notion in scientific theorizing and even that the only aim of the sciences is to enable us to predict future occurrences. This is sometimes linked with the view that the aim of science is a practical one, and opposed to the view that its aim is mainly the theoretical one of explaining and that prediction is subsidiary and subservient to this aim. This opposition is connected, somewhat indirectly, with the important controversy about whether the sciences can explain or whether they must be content with merely describing.

It must be noticed that not all hypothetical statements are hypotheses. "Hypothesis" is a scientific term indicating that something is being supposed to be true or is being entertained as a subject for investigation; "hypothetical" is a logical term which indicates that the statement referred to has a certain structure. A hypothesis may not be expressed in the hypothetical form and a hypothetical statement may not involve anything which would be an appropriate subject for scientific investigation. The fact that we often do use the "if . . . then . . ." form for hypotheses may lead us to confuse these two terms, but a little consideration soon reveals their difference.

The statement

$$\text{If } 2+2 = 4 \text{ and } 3+1 = 4 \text{ then } 2+2 = 3+1$$

is, as I have said, a hypothetical statement, but it is clearly not a hypothesis. The "If . . . then . . ." is used to draw attention to a relation between its three component statements and not to indicate either that we are *supposing* it to be true or that it is a possibility worth investigating. In fact, we neither entertain the possibility of its falsity nor suppose it to be in need of support.

12

THEORIES

In everyday discourse we are inclined to use the word "theory" in a loose and imprecise way to indicate anything from a hunch to a highly sophisticated and systematic structure of hypotheses. We may speak of a person as having a theory about the causes of road accidents and the police as having a theory about the identity of a murderer and, on the other hand, of Toynbee's theory of history and the Atomic Theory. In science and the philosophy of science we tend to speak more strictly, refusing to dignify simple hypotheses or mere hunches by the term.

On the whole, it is the practice of philosophers of science to regard a theory as a complex structure of connected hypotheses relating statements about observable phenomena which otherwise appear to be unrelated. Theories usually involve concepts which are not directly connected with observation. Thus we have the Kinetic Theory of Gases, which is a complex structure intended to exhibit the relations between, and explain, the very different sorts of behaviour displayed by gases under widely differing conditions.

It is worth considering, briefly and in crude outline, the form of this theory at one stage in its career. Certain general statements about the behaviour of gases under certain conditions, for example, Boyle's Law and Charles's Law, were arrived at empirically and accepted. It was seen that these statements could be connected by supposing that gases are composed of minute, unobserved particles having certain accurately specifiable properties; for example, they were conceived of as perfectly spherical, of negligible volume and moving at high speeds in straight lines. Each statement attributing one of these properties to the particles may be regarded as a separate hypothesis. Then, from these assumptions, together with the accepted laws of gravitation and the mechanics of such particles it could be deduced that, if the theory was correct, particular samples of gases would behave in various specifiable ways under various conditions. Most importantly, the behaviour of gases under varying conditions of temperature and pressure already covered by Boyle's Law and Charles's Law could be deduced. But it was also found that the same assumptions allowed the deduction of other behaviour under as yet unexamined conditions, for example, conditions allowing the diffusion of gases.

Thus the theory could be tested against both the known laws about gases and new observations under previously uninvestigated conditions suggested by the theory. Because the theory was complex and because the attributions of the various properties to the particles could, to some extent, be regarded as separate and independent hypotheses, there was considerable scope for the modification of the theory if it was found that the deduced consequences some-times failed to fit the observations.

The core of the theory was the postulation of the minute particles as constituents of gases. Their unobservability is important and, indeed, it can be argued that this contributes in an essential way to the explanatory power of the theory. Moreover, it allows us considerable room for manoeuvre. The restraints imposed on the theory by what is observed are directly imposed, as it were, only at the bottom of the structure and not at the top, upon the statements assigning the various properties to the particles. If there is any conflict between the theory and the observations we are free to modify the statements at the top until we obtain a better "fit".

Concepts of the unobservables of a theory or, more generally, concepts especially developed and intro-duced for the purposes of a theory and for the sake of their explanatory power are usually called *theoretical concepts*. Statements involving them are called *theoretical statements* and the postulated entities themselves are called *theoretical entities*. Theoretical statements are contrasted with *observation statements* or descriptive statements.

The consequences which are deduced from a theory, without the help of statements about particular instances and particular conditions, are general state-ments, such as, "The volume of a given mass of gas is inversely proportional to its pressure if the temperature is kept constant." In order to test this, and so test the theory, it is necessary to apply it to particular experimental or observational situations and to deduce statements about particular instances. This is necessary because we can only observe particular instances of behaviour. We can deduce statements about particular instances only with the help of *existential statements*, that is, statements which assert the existence, at a particular time and place, of the relevant objects, substances or conditions. For example, it is necessary to use our general statement along with some such statement as, "This vessel contains a gas and the apparatus is so arranged that the pressure and volume may vary while the temperature is kept constant", in order to deduce that *this* sample should behave in a specific way when the conditions are varied in a specific way relevant to the general statement. The statements which assert that the relevant conditions are fulfilled are *initial-condition statements*.

What has now been deduced is a consequence, or a set of consequences, of the theory applied to a particular observable situation. The final step in testing is the comparison of the description of what is observed, that is, of a collection of *observation statements*, with these deduced consequences. If the observation statements correspond with the deduced consequences, the deduced consequences are regarded as *verified* and the theory, to that extent, as *confirmed*; if not, the deduced consequences are regarded as *falsified* and the theory as *disconfirmed*. It is a common, but not invariable, practice to keep the terms "verified" and "falsified" for separate statements, especially those which are about directly observable things, and to use the terms "confirmed" and "disconfirmed" for theories.

It should be clear from what has gone before that to say that a theory is confirmed is not to say that it is established with finality and can never be modified or rejected. A theory may be confirmed to a greater or lesser extent, depending upon the extent to which its deduced consequences have been verified.

This account of theories leads to a number of questions in which philosophers of science are interested. There are certain problems, for example, about the logical relations between observation statements and the deduced consequences of theories. There are others concerning the precise effect upon a theory of the falsification of one of its deduced consequences. Still others concern the way in which theoretical concepts get their meanings and the justification for asserting or denying that theoretical statements refer to things which, although they are unobservable, really exist.

Theories are constructed in many different ways and the history of the development of a theory may not show clearly the logical structure of that theory. Some philosophers are interested in exhibiting this logical structure, in exploring the exact logical relations between its various statements, and this often necessitates the rewriting of the theory in its logical order rather than in the historical order of its development. The rewriting of a theory for this purpose is sometimes referred to as a *rational reconstruction* of the theory. This does not, of course, involve the addition of anything to the theory and is not intended to show either how the scientist works or how he ought to work; it is intended simply to be an aid to the better understanding of the logic of the sciences.

Perhaps the most general question, in this connection, concerns the ultimate aim of scientific theorizing. It has been held that scientific theories are *explanatory*, that they cannot be explanatory but only *descriptive*, and that they cannot be either explanatory or descriptive but are, at best, mere tools for predicting future occurrences. Here we are faced with questions of logic and meaning rather than questions about the beliefs of scientists. What are the criteria for saying that something is an explanation or a description and which of these criteria, if any, are satisfied by scientific theories? What precisely does it mean to say that the scientist predicts? Are there different types of prediction and how is prediction related to prophecy and guessing?

13

VERIFICATION AND FALSIFICATION; CONFIRMATION AND DISCONFIRMATION

As I have said, the testing of theories involves the attempt to verify or falsify their observable consequences, as a result of which the theories are confirmed or disconfirmed.

If it is thought that all scientific hypotheses are generalizations which can be expressed in the form

All *A* is *B*

then great weight may be given to the idea that we verify them by collecting large numbers of instances of *A*'s and finding that they are all *B*. The rationale of this is that if there is a finite number of *A*'s, then the nearer the number of observed *A*'s, constituting our evidence, approaches to this total number of *A*'s the greater is our justification for asserting that all *A*'s are *B*. Thus, one of the chief procedures of the sciences has been regarded as the collection and observation of large numbers of particular instances of whatever is being studied.

This view has been attacked in recent years, mainly for three reasons. First, it is said, a study of scientific procedures shows that scientists do not in fact spend much of their time making numerous observations of particular instances of what their hypotheses mention. Second, in testing many of the most important hypotheses, which are non-instantial, this procedure just could not be used. Third, it is doubtful if the scientist, when he states laws of the form "All A is B", is ever in the position to know that they refer to a finite number of A's, so that the alleged justification of this method of procedure is not forthcoming.

Whether we accept all these reasons or not, there are logical reasons for attaching more importance to the falsification of hypotheses than to their verification. Verification of a hypothesis can never be conclusive; if our hypothesis is about a finite number of A's there are practical difficulties in being sure that we have observed all of them, even ignoring possible future A's, but if our A's are infinite or not known to be finite, then it is logically impossible that verification should ever be conclusive. This is just the problem of induction. However, falsification is different, for it is possible to falsify conclusively a statement of the form "All A is B" merely by finding one A which is not B. Thus, falsification, as Bacon pointed out, enables us to reject a hypothesis of this form once and for all. This is a consequence of its generality and the meaning of "All A".

The view that there is asymmetry between verification and falsification is based on the belief that the logic of verification is inductive while that of falsification is deductive. This asymmetry is, it is said, communicated to the confirmation and disconfirmation of theories, which depend for their support on the verification or falsification of their deduced consequences.

Let p be a theory and q the conjunction of its deduced consequences, where both of these may be as complex, that is, composed of as many statements, as we wish. The theory is regarded as confirmed, to some extent at least, if the deduced consequences correspond with our observation statements, that is, if the deduced consequences are true. This, as I have said, may be represented by the inference-pattern

$$\text{If } p \text{ then } q$$
$$q$$
$$\therefore p$$

which, according to the rules of deductive inference, is invalid. This is to say that the support for p is inductive. But it is always possible for there to be alternative theories from which the same consequences are deducible, and we have here failed to rule out any of these alternatives. That is, the same observations would confirm an alternative theory s from which q is deducible. Then we have the inference-pattern

$$\text{If } s \text{ then } q$$
$$q$$
$$\therefore s.$$

Our observations may seem to give strong support to p just because we have not realized that there are possible alternatives, and the more possible alternatives we have thought of the less impressive is this support for p.

Moreover, there may be consequences of p which are deducible but which we have not deduced. "If p then q" may be consistent with "If p then r". It is possible to imagine the situation in which q was true and r false. Then q may appear to constitute strong support for p just because we have not seen that r is also deducible from p and so have not discovered that the true state of affairs conflicts with r and so with the theory. Thus confirmation can never be conclusive, because we may always have neglected alternative theories which allow the deduction of the same consequences, or neglected deductions we could have made from the theory we are trying to confirm. There is no way of ensuring that we have not done this.

Now consider disconfirmation. If it turns out that q conflicts with our observation statements we may reject our theory because what, according to this theory, should happen does not happen. The inference pattern, here, is

$$\text{If } p \text{ then } q$$
$$\text{Not } q$$
$$\therefore \text{ Not } p$$

which, as we have seen, is a valid deductive inference. This allows us to regard p as conclusively disconfirmed. At least we have succeeded in eliminating one possible theory. If there is a finite number of alternative theories and we know how many there are, there is the logical possibility of eliminating, in this way, all the alternatives except one which could then be regarded as strongly supported. Unfortunately, this is an ideal which it is usually impossible to realize. It may be that there is not a finite number of possible alternatives and certainly we can never know whether or not we have thought of all the possible alternatives.

Apart from this, the strength of falsification and disconfirmation is not as great as it has been made to appear and there is much more to be said about this. Clearly, a hypothesis which is a simple, categorical, universal statement of the form "All A is B" is conclusively refuted by a negative instance, that is, by an A which is not B; we know precisely what the negative instance forces us to reject. But many scientific hypotheses may not be appropriately represented by this form. More importantly, scientific theories are more complex than this. Their complexity often allows the rejection of only a part of a theory, and the disconfirmation of a theory may leave us with a choice between a large number of alternative modifications. That is, it forces us to reject *something* without telling us precisely what. Thus, what disconfirmation can give us certainty about is specified only within rather widely-spaced limits, and the spacing of these limits will vary with the complexity of the theory.

14

PROBABILITY

When we say that scientific conclusions cannot be established with certainty, or conclusively proved, it seems reasonable to say that these conclusions are *probably* true and to talk of the *probability* of their truth. When we say that we can never be sure that an event predicted on the basis of evidence or a theory will occur it often seems reasonable to say that this event will *probably* occur and to talk of the *probability* of its occurrence. Immediately, questions arise as to the meaning of "probably" and "probability" and as to methods of estimating or measuring probability in those contexts, and some philosophers of science regard these as among the central questions of the subject.

Immediately, there is a distinction to be made which is implicit in the last paragraph. We must distinguish between the probability of a hypothesis or a theory and the probability of an event. This is essentially the distinction between the probability that a given statement is true and the probability that a given event will occur. Some theories themselves embody probability statements, that is, statements to the effect that there is a definite probability that a certain event will occur under certain conditions;

other theories embody no such statements. Statistical hypotheses are, or contain, probability statements. For example, it is a hypothesis of modern physics that there is a probability of $\frac{1}{2}$ that a radium atom will disintegrate within 1,700 years. That is, the theory of which this statement is a part contains statements about the probability of the occurrence of certain events.

However, this theory and, indeed, any other theory or hypothesis, may be regarded as probable in another sense, that it is likely to be true, that it would be reasonable to accept it or that it would be more reasonable to accept it than any other theory or hypothesis covering the same phenomena.

It is, on the whole, generally accepted that it is possible to give numerical estimates of the probability of events and there are elaborate probability theories which aim to enable us to do this. It is more difficult to see how it is possible to make the concept of the probability of a hypothesis or theory quantitative, although there have been attempts to do so.

Concerning the estimation of the probability of events, we may distinguish two main kinds of probability calculations, namely *a priori* and *a posteriori* calculations. These have been regarded as rival mathematical theories of probability and as merely different kinds of calculations appropriate to different situations. I shall not consider the merits of the various views; the literature is enormous and it would be impossible to do justice to it here.

A priori probability can best be explained by considering the throwing of ordinary dice. A perfect die is a cube which is completely regular in shape and weight, with no bias of any sort towards one face, and having one number only on each face. If it is thrown in a random way then no one face is more likely than the others to be uppermost when it comes to rest. There are six possibilities and the probability of any specified number being uppermost is one in six, represented by the fraction $\frac{1}{6}$. This is, of course, the same for each number, if the die is perfect. If we bet on the throwing of, say, a three, in one throw, then the throwing of the three is the *favourable possibility* from among the six *total possibilities*. In this situation the probability is given by the fraction

$$\frac{\text{Number of favourable possibilities}}{\text{Total number of possibilities}}$$

It is clear that given the assumptions we have made, it is possible to work out the probability of many other occurrences under various conditions. For example, we can give formulae for calculating the probability of a given number being thrown with two or three or four or n dice, for calculating the probability of the same number being thrown twice in succession with one or more dice, and so on. These are *a priori* calculations because they do not depend upon the observing of what has happened when actual dice have been thrown. They are based purely upon the characteristics we assign to perfect dice and the conditions we specify. Similar calculations can be made of the probability, for example, of a randomly dealt hand of cards containing only one suit or of someone's picking only white balls out of a bag containing black and white balls in various proportions. These calculations all depend upon the definition of the situation and not upon any actual state of affairs.

Now consider the kind of calculation of probability made by actuaries on behalf of insurance companies. It is important for insurance companies to know what premium they can economically charge for life insurance. This depends upon the number of years for which an insured person can be expected to pay a premium in relation to the sum assured, and this depends upon when he begins to pay and when he is going to die. But nobody can tell, for certain, when he is going to die. It is important, therefore, that there shall be some method of assessing the probability of his dying within a certain period of years. The actuary bases his estimate of any given person's dying before he is, say, 70, assuming good health, upon the proportion of men in good health at the time of insuring who have died before they were 70, in recent years. If it is found, for example, that one man in four has died before he was 70 in the past ten years, he will be fairly safe in saying that, barring accidents and epidemics, the probability of a particular man now dying before he is 70 is 1 in 4 or $\frac{1}{4}$. Premiums would be calculated accordingly.

This estimate of probability is *a posteriori* because it depends upon past experience and upon the assumption that it is reasonable to suppose that what has happened for a number of years in the immediate past will, roughly, go on happening in the future. It is not based upon the definition of an ideal situation but upon the observation of actual situations. This kind of calculation is sometimes called a "frequency" calculation, since it depends on the frequency with which a specified event has occurred in the past.

It should be noted that there are two parts to the actuary's calculation. On the one hand, there is a statement which is merely a description of what has happened in the past; on the other hand, there is a prediction, based on this, of what is likely to happen in the future. The first statement is merely descriptive and makes no predictions, the second is inductive rather than descriptive.

In either of these calculations, the value 0 would indicate that there was no probability whatever of the event's occurring, that is, that it could not possibly occur; a value of 1 would indicate that the probability of its occurring amounted to a necessity, that is, that it must occur and that we should be entitled to be certain that it would. For example, the probability of the number 10 being thrown with a die with only the numbers 1 to 6 on it is $\frac{0}{6} = 0$; the probability of the number 1 being thrown with a die having the number 1 on each side is $\frac{6}{6} = 1$.

Now, of course, besides making *a priori* calculations about perfect dice we may throw actual dice and see what happens. We may make *a posteriori* calculations about the probability of throwing a certain number with a particular die, based upon what has happened on previous throwings of that die. The results of these calculations may differ greatly from the results of *a priori* calculations. We might find that in the course of a million throws the number 3 was thrown only ten thousand times and in consequence say that the probability of throwing a 3 on any subsequent throw was

$$\frac{10,000}{1,000,000} = \frac{1}{100},$$

whereas the *a priori* probability, given a perfect die, is $\frac{1}{6}$.

This discrepancy might show that the die was biassed, i.e., not perfect, or that the throwing was biassed, or it might show neither of these things. We might find that if we threw the same die several million more times we would get a fraction of $\frac{1}{6}$. The question concerning what ought to happen if we did throw a die which was known to be perfect involves questions about what *a priori* probability calculations mean in relation to physical situations, whether they can be applied to physical situations and what is the relation between *a priori* and *a posteriori* calculations. These are large questions which cannot be discussed here. We must bear in mind, however, that we are dealing with two different conceptions of probability. It seems plausible to suppose that the *a posteriori* conception is more relevant to scientific prediction than the *a priori* conception. But it should not be supposed that there is only one kind of *a posteriori* calculation of probability and more complex kinds of calculation have been thought to be more suitable for scientific contexts.

I now turn to the *probability of statements*, that is, the probability that a given hypothesis or theory is true. If we say that a hypothesis or theory is probably true are we using "probably" in a sense which allows a calculation of the probability? Some writers have denied that it is possible to give a value to this sort of probability, others have attempted to show how it can be done. One thing that we must note is that the probability of a hypothesis is always relative to the evidence we have for it. In itself, a hypothesis is either true or false and neither probable nor improbable. It makes sense to talk of it as probable only if we mean that on the evidence we have, the hypothesis is probably true. Thus a given hypothesis may be more probable at one time than another; relative to the evidence we have now it may be more probable than it was relative to the evidence we had a year ago.

We can see at once that there are difficulties. How are we to measure *amounts* of evidence? We can say that if we have a great deal of evidence supporting a hypothesis then the probability of its truth is high.

But whether a given body of evidence is to count as "a great deal" depends on its relation to all the evidence there could be for the hypothesis; if the evidence we have is only a tiny fraction of the total possible evidence, is it a great deal? And what does "the total evidence" mean?

Consider one of the simpler sorts of hypotheses first. Suppose we think it true that all gorillas now living like dates. Suppose also that we know that there are only 100 gorillas now living and that 90 of these like dates and we have no information about the rest. Can we give a numerical probability of the truth of our generalization? Should we say that out of 90 observed gorillas 90 like dates, so the probability of all liking dates is $\frac{90}{90} = 1$? This surely can't be right, since there must be some possibility of some of the unobserved gorillas not liking dates. Then should we say that out of 100 gorillas 90 like dates, so the probability of all liking dates is $\frac{90}{100}$? This appears to give too little weight to the evidence we have and to the possibility that all or some of the unobserved gorillas like dates.

Consider two situations.

(1) We have found that 10 gorillas like dates but we have no information about the other 90.

(2) We have found that 90 gorillas like dates but we have no information about the other 10.

We can at least say that in the second situation we have

more justification than in the first for saying that all gorillas like dates. That is, on the evidence we have, the probability of all gorillas liking dates is higher than in the first situation. The larger the proportion of the total we know about, the more justification we have for pronouncing upon the whole. What is difficult is to assign a value to the probabilities. It is difficult because in such a situation the unexamined cases are quite unknown; the evidence we have gives us absolutely no information about the unexamined cases.

Now, this is a highly artificial kind of hypothesis and if the assessment of its probability presents difficulties, the assessment of the probability of any hypothesis which scientists in fact consider presents even greater ones. Any actual hypothesis which can be put in the form "All A is B" is likely to be of unrestricted generality for it is likely to be about all past and future A's as well as present ones. In particular, it is most unlikely to be about just 100 A's, or any other specifiable number. This means that, at the very best, we do not know how many A's we are referring to and that, at the worst, we are referring to an infinitely large collection.

If we take the hypothesis to cover an infinitely large collection, then the denominator of our probability fraction would presumably be infinity and then, whatever the numerator, that is, however much evidence we have, the probability of our hypothesis must be *zero*, which is a strange result. On the other hand, if we take the hypothesis to cover a finite but unknown collection we do not know what figure to put as the denominator of our probability fraction and so can make no estimate.

Moreover, in either case, the evidence we have may be only a minute fraction of the evidence we could have, that is, it may be based on only a minute fraction of the total number of cases. Then although we want to say that the more evidence we have the more likely our conclusions are to be true we can never be sure that the amount of evidence we have is not utterly insignificant. So perhaps even a comparative statement about non-quantitative probability has little point. This kind of consideration has led people to say that it is just inappropriate to talk of the probability of scientific hypotheses or laws. Nevertheless, it does seem absurd to deny that the more evidence we have for a conclusion the less likely we are to be mistaken in that conclusion.

Thus there remain problems, and so rival schools of thought, upon the question of the importance of probability in connection with the conclusions of science. There are those who hold that the problems to which I have drawn attention are the consequence of too naïve an approach and require for their solution a more subtle account of probability. Others attempt to give an interpretation of laws and theories according to which it does not make sense to talk of them as either true or false, either probable or improbable. For example, it is held by some that laws are rules for inferring rather than assertions about the world, and by others that their relation to the world is comparable to the relation of a map to a stretch of country rather than to the relation of a statement to a fact.

15

OBSERVATION

It is usually thought that observation plays an important part in the sciences, both in posing the problems which require scientific investigation and in testing the hypotheses and theories which result from that investigation. Indeed, the terms "natural sciences" and "observational sciences" are often used interchangeably. The term "observation", in this context at least, is a blanket term covering the use of the five senses; we may observe by seeing, hearing, feeling, smelling and tasting. In the sciences, seeing and hearing are by far the most important means of observing. However, "observing" carries with it the suggestion that the procedure is careful and methodical, the suggestion that observing is not mere noticing but involves the *examination* of what is observed.

The traditional inductivist account of the sciences tends to assert that they have their origins in our noticing, in the course of our everyday activities, interesting regularities and puzzling irregularities in natural events. According to this account, we begin to be scientific when we pass from mere noticing to the careful and systematic examination of these regularities and irregularities with a view to making general statements about them. Moreover, observation not only involves this careful and systematic procedure but must also be openminded and unprejudiced, unaffected by preconceived ideas. As is well known, it is all too easy to see what we hope or expect to see, and the training of the scientist must enable him to discount the effects of his hopes and expectations.

Contrasted with this cool and unprejudiced observation was *interpretation*. If we are all capable of learning to make such observations then statements recording them can form the agreed starting-points for scientific investigation. But as soon as we leave statements of this sort, interpretation begins and agreement is no longer assured, although it is hoped for. As soon as we leave the firm ground of what is observable by every unprejudiced observer we are more or less at the mercy of our personal knowledge, accepted beliefs and favoured hypotheses, which are likely to influence the way in which we systematize and explain. So, it is held, the scientist must attempt to keep as close as possible for as long as possible to the observable facts, in an attempt to accept as conclusions only those statements upon which everyone with eyes to see and ears to hear can agree.

When there are disagreements, the only sure way of settling them is to return to the observed facts, because this is our only common ground. A hypothesis upon which there is little agreement may be rendered acceptable by developing instruments, such as telescopes or microscopes, which enable us to observe something which is mentioned in the hypothesis but which was not previously observable. Those who refused to look through Galileo's telescope, whatever other reasons they had, perhaps recognized the power of this procedure and feared the establishment of his hypothesis and the consequent overthrow of theirs. Hypotheses which are not directly testable by observation leave room for disagreement whereas those which are directly testable by observation do not.

This view that observation lies at the beginning and end of all science is sometimes called, pejoratively, "observationalism", and has, in recent years, come in for considerable criticism. The main ground for this is that, it is said, it is impossible to draw a sharp line between observation and interpretation and, more strongly, it is impossible to make what may be called a "pure" observation statement. Every alleged observation statement involves some kind of interpretation depending upon existing knowledge, unquestioned beliefs and accepted theories. Two people who describe a man exhibiting certain symptoms as suffering from smallpox will be interpreting the situation quite differently if one believes that smallpox involves infection by certain bacteria and the other believes that it involves the intervention of some supernatural agency.

It has even been argued that not only what we say but also what we see covertly involves interpretation. Some of the "ambiguous figures" used by psychologists give support to this view. There is, for example, a well-known drawing which can be seen as a drawing of either a duck or a rabbit. But a person who had never seen a rabbit and knew nothing about animals of this sort could not see it as a drawing of a rabbit; he would not have the necessary basis for making this interpretation. If what we see depends upon what we already know or believe, then it should not be surprising if our statements recording what we see have this knowledge and these beliefs "built into" them.

Thus, it is said, science cannot be held to be based on bare, unprejudiced observations and statements recording these observations. On the contrary, it begins with the entertaining of hypotheses which observation is intended to test. Scientific observation involves the selection of what is relevant and relevance must be determined by some hypothesis; the hypothesis guides our observation by providing something to which certain observable things are relevant while others are not. We cannot avoid entertaining hypotheses; a scientist is a person who is not content until he can produce evidence for the retention or the rejection of his hypotheses.

Those who accept this account deny induction an important place, or even any place whatever, in the sciences. According to them, the method of the sciences is *hypothetico-deductive*, that is, the method of deducing the consequences of entertained hypotheses and undertaking observation with the aim of showing these hypotheses to be untenable or tenable. Observations are to be interpreted in the light of hypotheses and observations which cannot be so interpreted count against these hypotheses and constitute the basis for their rejection. Whether or not this view entails the rejection of the logic, as well as the procedure, of induction is a matter for further discussion.

EPILOGUE

There are, indeed, numerous matters for further discussion, and I must again emphasize the elementary nature of the foregoing comments. Almost every logical concept is more complex than it appears to be in this little book, and my aim has been to establish the minimum familiarity with these concepts necessary for introductory courses in the philosophy and the history of science. Further study in the purely logical field is advisable and I have referred in the bibliography to various larger logical treatises.

I have mentioned in passing many questions in the philosophy of science itself, some of which are almost certain to receive attention in any introductory course on this subject. I have been forced, because of the scope of the work, to refer sometimes to things philosophers say without making it clear why they say them. This is a state of affairs which is not to be tolerated by anyone with the slightest philosophical inclination; I have accordingly listed in the bibliography works in which such a person may begin to satisfy his curiosity if no lecturer is available to do it for him, or if any available lecturer fails to do it adequately.

BIBLIOGRAPHY

1. LOGIC: ELEMENTARY

SINCLAIR, A., *The Traditional Formal Logic*, Methuen.

STEBBING, L. S., *A Modern Elementary Logic*, 5th ed., revised by C. W. K. Mundle, Methuen (1952).

KEENE, G. B., *Language and Reasoning*, Van Nostrand, (1961).

BASSON, A. H., *and* O'CONNOR, D. J., *Introduction to Symbolic Logic*, revised, University Tutorial Press (1957).

2. LOGIC: MORE ADVANCED

JOSEPH, H. W. B., *An Introduction to Logic*, Oxford (1906).

This is an Aristotelian account of logic and includes interesting discussions of predication, definition and other subjects touched upon in the present book.

ŁUKASIEWICZ, J., *Aristotle's Syllogistic*, Oxford (1951).

An important discussion of Aristotelian logic from the modern standpoint.

EATON, R. M., *General Logic*, Scribner (1931).

This is perhaps the clearest and most readable general introduction to logic. It is particularly useful for a lucid account of some modern developments in logic.

COHEN, M. R., *and* NAGEL, E., *An Introduction to Logic and Scientific Method*, Routledge and Kegan Paul (1934).

STEBBING, L. S., *A Modern Introduction to Logic*, Methuen (1930).

These are both standard textbooks covering most of the subjects discussed.

BLACK, M., *Critical Thinking*, Prentice-Hall (1946).

A highly original and stimulating introduction.

SUPPES, P., *Introduction to Logic*, Van Nostrand (1957).

An excellent introduction to contemporary symbolic logic.

NIDDITCH, P., *Elementary Logic of Science and Mathematics*, University Tutorial Press (1960).

An account of the logic of arguments which are actually used in mathematics and the sciences.

STRAWSON, P. F., *Introduction to Logical Theory*, Methuen (1952).

An important examination of the basic principles of formal logic.

TOULMIN, S. E., *The Uses of Argument*, Cambridge (1958).
An introduction to anti-Logic.

3. THE PHILOSOPHY OF SCIENCE

NAGEL, E., *The Structure of Science*, Routledge and Kegan Paul (1961).
A comprehensive survey of the problems.

DANTO, A., *and* MORGENBESSER, S. (Editors), *Philosophy of Science*, Meridian Books (1960).
A collection of essays and extracts by many authorities.

POPPER, K. R., *The Logic of Scientific Discovery*, Hutchinson (1959).

The anti-inductivist's bible.

RUSSELL, B., *The Problems of Philosophy*, Williams & Norgate (1912); *Human Knowledge*, Allen and Unwin (1948).

These contain two different approaches to the problem of induction. *Human Knowledge* has a useful introductory discussion of various views of probability.

KNEALE, W. C., *Probability and Induction*, Oxford (1949). Essential reading on this subject.

REICHENBACH, H., *Experience and Prediction*, Chicago (1938) and Phoenix Books (1961).

BRAITHWAITE, R. B., *Scientific Explanation*, Cambridge (1957) and Harper Torchbooks (1960).

An account of the formal structure of scientific theories.

TOULMIN, S. E., *The Philosophy of Science*, Hutchinson (1953).

HANSON, N. R., *Patterns of Discovery*, Cambridge (1958).

ALEXANDER, P., *Sensationalism and Scientific Explanation*, Routledge and Kegan Paul (1963).

Mentioned only for the clues it provides to the author's prejudices.

4. GENERAL PHILOSOPHY

Books have been included here either because they deal more fully with matters discussed in the present work or because they help to set the contemporary philosophical scene.

AUSTIN, J., *Philosophical Papers*, Oxford (1962); *Sense and Sensibilia*, Oxford (1962).

AYER, A. J., *Language, Truth and Logic*, Gollancz (1936).

COHEN, L. J., *The Diversity of Meaning*, Methuen (1962),

GOODMAN, N., *Fact, Fiction and Forecast*, London U.P. (1954).

KÖRNER, S., *The Philosophy of Mathematics*, Hutchinson (1960).

PRICE, H. H., *Thinking and Experience*, Hutchinson (1953).

QUINE, W. V., *From a Logical Point of View*, Harvard (1956); *Word and Object*, M.I.T. (1960).

RYLE, G., *The Concept of Mind*, Hutchinson (1949).

STRAWSON, P. F., *Individuals*, Methuen (1959).

WISDOM, J., *Philosophy and Psycho-Analysis*, Blackwell (1953).

WITTGENSTEIN, L., *The Blue and Brown Books*, Blackwell (1958); *Philosophical Investigations*, Blackwell (1953).

ZIFF, P., *Semantic Analysis*, Cornell (1960).

INDEX